# Chapters 1–5 Resources

**Glencoe**

New York, New York    Columbus, Ohio    Chicago, Illinois    Peoria, Illinois    Woodland Hills, California

A Glencoe Program

# PHYSICS
## Principles and Problems

**Student Edition**

**Teacher Wraparound Edition**

**Teacher Chapter Resources**
Mini Lab Worksheets
Physics Lab Worksheets
Study Guide
Section Quizzes
Reinforcement
Enrichment
Transparency Masters
Transparency Worksheets
Chapter Assessment

**Teacher Classroom Resources**
Teaching Transparencies
Laboratory Manual, Student Edition
Laboratory Manual, Teacher Edition
Probeware Laboratory Manual, Student Edition
Probeware Laboratory Manual, Teacher Edition
Forensics Laboratory Manual, Student Edition

Forensics Laboratory Manual, Teacher Edition
Supplemental Problems
Additional Challenge Problems
Pre-AP/Critical Thinking Problems
Physics Test Prep: Studying for the End-of-Course Exam, Student Edition
Physics Test Prep: Studying for the End-of-Course Exam, Teacher Edition
Connecting Math to Physics
Solutions Manual

**Technology**
Answer Key Maker
Exam*View*® Pro
Interactive Chalkboard
McGraw-Hill Learning Network
StudentWorks™ CD-ROM
TeacherWorks™ CD-ROM
**physicspp.com** Web site

 **Glencoe**

The *McGraw-Hill* Companies

Send all inquiries to:
Glencoe/McGraw-Hill
8787 Orion Place
Columbus, Ohio 43240

ISBN 0-07-865902-7

Printed in the United States of America

3 4 5 6 7 8 9  045  09 08 07 06

# Contents

## Chapters 1–5 Resources

# To the Teacher

This book contains resources that support five Student Edition chapters of *Physics: Principles and Problems.* The worksheets and activities have been developed to help you teach these chapters more effectively. You will find in chapter order:

## REPRODUCIBLE PAGES

### HANDS-ON ACTIVITIES

**Mini Lab and Physics Lab Worksheets:** These worksheets are expanded versions of the Mini Labs and Physics Labs that appear in the five Student Edition chapters supported in this book. All materials lists, procedures, and questions are repeated so that students can complete a lab in most cases without having a textbook on the lab table. Data tables are enlarged so they can be used to easily record data, and all lab questions are reprinted with lines on which students can write their answers. For student safety, all appropriate safety symbols and caution statements have been reproduced on these pages. Answer pages for each Mini Lab and Physics Lab Worksheet are included in the Teacher Guide and Answers section at the back of this book.

### EXTENSION AND INTERVENTION

**Study Guide:** These pages help your students learn physics vocabulary and concepts. Study Guide worksheets typically consist of six pages of questions and exercises for each of the five Student Edition chapters supported in this book. Items are presented in a variety of objective formats: matching, true/false, interpreting diagrams and data, multiple choice, short-answer questions, and so on. The first Study Guide worksheet for each chapter reviews vocabulary. Subsequent worksheets closely follow the organization of the textbook, providing review items for each textbook section and references to specific content.

Students will find the Study Guide worksheets helpful for previewing or reviewing chapter material. As a preview, the worksheets help students focus on the concepts at the time you assign the reading. Students can complete each Study Guide section after reading the corresponding textbook section. Some students will have more success completing the sheets in smaller chunks. For this reason, the question sets on the Study Guide pages are referenced to specific readings in the textbook. When complete, these worksheets will prove to be an excellent review instrument. Answers to the Study Guide pages are included in the Teacher Guide and Answers section at the back of this book.

**Reinforcement:** These pages provide opportunities that complete your teaching cycle and benefit all your students. Reinforcement masters are especially helpful for students who require additional instruction in order to understand certain concepts. A Reinforcement master is provided for each of the five Student Edition chapters supported in this book. Answers to these pages are included in the Teacher Guide and Answers section at the back of this book.

**Enrichment:** These activities offer students the chance to apply physics concepts to new situations. Students explore high-interest topics in a variety of formats. Some of the masters are hands-on activities. An Enrichment master is provided for each of the five Student Edition chapters supported in this book. Answers to these pages are included in the Teacher Guide and Answers section at the back of this book.

# To the Teacher

*continued*

## TRANSPARENCY ACTIVITIES

**Teaching Transparency Masters and Activities:**
These transparencies relate to major concepts that will benefit from an extra visual learning aid. Most of the transparencies contain art or photos that extend the concepts put forth by those in the textbook. Others contain art or photos directly from the Student Edition. There are 120 Teaching Transparencies. The ones that support these five Student Edition chapters are provided here as black-and-white masters accompanied by worksheets that review the concepts presented in the transparencies. Teaching Tips for some transparencies and answers to all worksheet questions are provided in the Teacher Guide and Answers section at the back of this book.

## ASSESSMENT

**Section Quiz:** The Section Quiz page consists of questions or problems that focus on key content from one section of the Student Edition. Each quiz typically includes conceptual items that require a written response or explanation and items that require problem-solving skills or mathematical calculations, where applicable. The Section Quiz offers representative practice items that allow you to monitor your students' understanding of the textbook. Answers to each Section Quiz are provided in the Teacher Guide and Answers section at the back of this book.

**Chapter Assessment:** The Chapter Assessment pages provide materials to evaluate your students' understanding of concepts and content from the five Student Edition chapters supported in this book. Each test consists of six pages of material, which is divided into three sections.

■ Understanding Physics Concepts requires students to demonstrate their knowledge of vocabulary and other basic information presented in the chapter. They are assessed through a variety of question types, including matching, modified true/false, short answer/fill-in, and multiple choice.

■ Thinking Critically requires students to use higher-order learning skills. Students will need to interpret data and discover relationships presented in graphs and tables. Other questions may require them to apply their understanding of concepts to solve problems, compare or contrast situations, and make inferences or predictions.

■ Applying Physics Knowledge consists of items that assess students' ability to extend their learning to new situations. Assessment is done qualitatively through short-answer questions, and quantitatively through problems. The questions and problems in this section are more difficult than those presented earlier and generally require more calculations as well as a deeper comprehension of chapter concepts.

## TEACHER GUIDE AND ANSWERS

Answers or possible answers to all worksheet questions and activities can be found in order of appearance at the back of this book. Criteria for acceptable answers are found where appropriate.

# Reproducible Pages Contents

## A Physics Toolkit

**CHAPTER**

# 1 ⎯ Mini Lab Worksheet

## Measuring Change  👓 ✋

Collect five identical washers and a spring that will stretch measurably when one washer is suspended from it.

1. **Measure** the length of the spring with zero, one, two, and three washers suspended from it.
2. **Graph** the length of the spring versus the mass in the space below.
3. **Predict** the length of the spring with four and five washers.
4. **Test** your prediction.

## Analyze and Conclude

5. **Describe** the shape of the graph. How did you use it to predict the two new lengths?

_____

_____

_____

_____

*Physics: Principles and Problems*

**CHAPTER**

# 1 — Physics Lab Worksheet

**Materials**

• Internet access is required.

• watch or other timer

## Exploring Objects in Motion

Physics is a science that is based upon experimental observations. Many of the basic principles used to describe and understand mechanical systems, such as objects in linear motion, can be applied later to describe more complex natural phenomena. How can you measure the speed of the vehicles in a video clip?

### Question

What types of measurements could be made to find the speed of a vehicle?

### Objectives

■ **Observe** the motion of the vehicles seen in the video.

■ **Describe** the motion of the vehicles.

■ **Collect** and **organize data** on the vehicle's motion.

■ **Calculate** a vehicle's speed.

| Data Table | | | |
|---|---|---|---|
| **Marker** | **Distance (km)** | **White Vehicle Time (s)** | **Gray Pickup Time (s)** |
| | | | |
| | | | |
| | | | |
| | | | |

## Procedure

1. Visit **physicspp.com/internet_lab** to view the Chapter 1 lab video clip.

2. The video footage was taken in the midwestern United States at approximately noon. Along the right shoulder of the road are large, white, painted rectangles. These types of markings are used in many states for aerial observation of traffic. They are placed at 0.322-km (0.2-mi) intervals.

3. **Observe** What type of measurements might be taken? Prepare a data table, such as the one shown above. Record your observations of the surroundings, other vehicles, and markings. On what color vehicle is the camera located, and what color is the pickup truck in the lane to the left?

_____

_____

4. **Measure and Estimate** View the video again and look for more details. Is the road smooth? In what direction are the vehicles heading? How long does it take each vehicle to travel two intervals marked by the white blocks? Record your observations and data.

_____

_____

_____

## Analyze

1. Summarize your qualitative observations.

_____

_____

2. Summarize your quantitative observations.

_____

_____

3.  **Make and Use Graphs**  Graph both sets of data on one pair of axes.

4.  **Estimate**  What is the speed of the vehicles in km/s and km/h?

5.  **Predict**  How far will each vehicle travel in 5 min?

## Conclude and Apply

1.  **Measure**  What is the precision of the distance and time measurements?

    _____

    _____

    _____

2.  **Measure**  What is the precision of your speed measurement? On what does it depend?

    _____

    _____

    _____

3.  **Use Variables, Constants, and Controls**  Describe the independent and the dependent variables in this experiment.

    _____

    _____

    _____

4.  **Compare and Contrast**  Which vehicle's graph has a steeper slope? What is the slope equal to?

    _____

    _____

    _____

**5.** **Infer** What would a horizontal line mean on the graph? A line with a steeper slope?

_____

_____

_____

## Going Further

Speed is distance traveled divided by the amount of time to travel that distance. Explain how you could design your own experiment to measure speed in the classroom using remote-controlled cars. What would you use for markers? How precisely could you measure distance and time? Would the angle at which you measured the cars passing the markers affect the results? How much? How could you improve your measurements? What units make sense for speed? How far into the future could you predict the cars' positions? If possible, carry out the experiment and summarize your results.

_____

_____

_____

## Real-World Physics

When the speedometer is observed by a front-seat passenger, the driver, and a passenger in the rear driver's-side seat, readings of 90 km/h, 100 km/h, and 110 km/h, respectively, are observed. Explain the differences.

_____

_____

## Share Your Data

**Design an Experiment** Visit **physicspp.com/internet_lab** to post your experiment for measuring speed in the classroom using remote-controlled cars. Include your list of materials, your procedure, and your predictions for the accuracy of your lab. If you actually perform your lab, post your data and results as well.

**Physics** nline

To find out more about measurement, visit the
Web site: **physicspp.com**

# CHAPTER 1 Study Guide

## A Physics Toolkit
### Vocabulary Review

*Write the term that correctly completes the statement. Use each term once.*

| | | | |
|---|---|---|---|
| accuracy | independent variable | measurement | significant digits |
| dependent variable | inverse relationship | physics | scientific law |
| dimensional analysis | line of best fit | precision | scientific method |
| hypothesis | linear relationship | quadratic relationship | scientific theory |

**1.** _____ The study of matter and energy is _____.

**2.** _____ The _____ is a systematic way to observe, experiment, and analyze the world.

**3.** _____ The valid digits in a measurement are called the _____.

**4.** _____ A(n) _____ describes the relationship between two variables in which an increase in one variable results in the decrease of another variable.

**5.** _____ On a graph, the _____ is the line drawn as close as possible to all of the data points.

**6.** _____ A(n) _____ is an educated guess about how variables are related.

**7.** _____ The _____ is the factor that is changed or manipulated during an experiment.

**8.** _____ A(n) _____ is description of a rule of nature.

**9.** _____ A(n) _____ is a comparison between an unknown quantity and a standard.

**10.** _____ A straight line on a graph shows that there is a(n) _____ between the two variables.

**11.** _____ A(n) _____ is an explanation supported by experimental results.

**12.** _____ _____ describes how well the results of a measurement agree with the real value.

**13.** _____ The _____ is the factor that depends on the independent variable.

**14.** _____ The method of treating units as algebraic quantities, which can be cancelled, is called _____.

**15.** _____ A(n) _____ exists when one variable depends on the square of another.

**16.** _____ The degree of exactness of a measurement is called _____.

## Section 1.1 ⬤ Mathematics and Physics

In your textbook, read about mathematics in physics on pages 4–5.
*Write the term that correctly completes the statement. Use each term once.*

| | | |
|---|---|---|
| dimensional analysis | experiments | theories |
| equations | graphs | units |
| experimental data | results | |

Physicists do **(1)** _____, make observations, and collect

**(2)** _____. They predict the **(3)** _____ using different

models. They create **(4)** _____ to describe their observations. Due to the

mathematical nature of their work, physicists can enter numbers into **(5)** _____

to model observations and make predictions. The numerical values in an equation are also described by

**(6)** _____, such as amperes, ohms, and volts. **(7)** _____

is the method of treating the units as algebraic quantities, which can be cancelled. Varying numerical

results from equations can be plotted as **(8)** _____.

In your textbook, read about SI units on pages 5–6.
*For each term on the left, write the letter of the matching item on the right.*

_____ **9.** base quantity of temperature

_____ **10.** base quantity of electric current

_____ **11.** base quantity of length

_____ **12.** base quantity of time

_____ **13.** base amount of a substance

_____ **14.** pico

_____ **15.** centi

_____ **16.** micro

_____ **17.** mega

**a.** meter
**b.** $10^{-2}$
**c.** kelvin
**d.** $10^{-12}$
**e.** ampere
**f.** second
**g.** $10^{6}$
**h.** mole
**i.** $10^{-6}$

In your textbook, read about significant digits on page 7.

*For each of the statements below, write* **true** *or rewrite the italicized part to make the statement true.*

**18.** _____ When you perform any arithmetic operation and round off the last digit, this is the *most* precise part of the measurement.

**19.** _____ The figure 0.0730 has *two* significant digits.

**20.** _____ Answers derived with a calculator should be written *exactly as they appear on the calculator.*

In your textbook, read about scientific methods on pages 8–10.

*Number the following steps in the order in which scientists study problems.*

_____ **21.** Draw a conclusion.

_____ **22.** Compare experimentation with careful measurements and analyses of results.

_____ **23.** Test deductions to determine if they are valid.

*Indicate which step in the scientific method best describes the statements in questions 24–29. Explain your answers. Use complete sentences.*

**24.** A basketball is rolling on the ground. It continues to move even though no one is pushing it.

_____

_____

**25.** The velocity of the rolling basketball is 0.5 m/s.

_____

_____

**26.** In an isolated system, momentum does not change. For example, when a bowling ball hits a rolling basketball, the bowling ball slows down and the basketball speeds up. The increase in momentum of the basketball equals the decrease in momentum of the bowling ball.

_____

_____

**27.** There are two tracks that you can roll the basketball on. One track is very steep and the other is nearly flat. You guess that the basketball will travel faster down the steep track.

_____

_____

**28.** After recording the speeds of a basketball rolling down a steep track and on a flat track, you repeat the experiment, timing the ball a second time.

_____

_____

**29.** You observe multiple collisions between a basketball and a bowling ball and record data on their post collision velocities and directions. You explain your idea that since the bowling ball has a greater mass and is moving at greater velocity, it can always change the direction of the basketball that has a smaller mass and is moving at a slower velocity.

_____

_____

## Section 1.2   Measurement

In your textbook, read about measurement on pages 11–14.

*Circle the letter of the choice that best completes the statement.*

**1.** The apparent shift in position of an object when it is viewed from various angles is called _____.

   **a.** parallax

   **b.** margin of error

   **c.** calibration

   **d.** accuracy

**2.** A device with very small divisions on its scale can measure with _____.

   **a.** scientific notation

   **b.** agreement

   **c.** precision

   **d.** fundamental units

**3.** An atomic mass unit is measured at $1.660 \times 10^{-27}$ kg, a number that has _____ significant digits.

   **a.** 1

   **b.** 2

   **c.** 3

   **d.** 4

**4.** The NIST-Fl Cesium Fountain clock in Colorado is our standard for _____.

   **a.** significant digits

   **b.** accuracy

   **c.** measuring instruments

   **d.** calculating errors

**5.** A comparison between an unknown quantity and a standard is referred to as a _____.

   **a.** margin of error

   **b.** consistency

   **c.** measurement

   **d.** variables

**6.** _____ is a technique used to assure the accuracy of a measuring instrument.

   **a.** Two-point calibration

   **b.** Precision

   **c.** Analysis

   **d.** Dimension

**7.** The degree of possible error in a measurement is called its _____.

   **a.** fundamental unit

   **b.** mechanical quantity

   **c.** precision balance

   **d.** margin of uncertainty

**Section 1.3** **Graphing Data**

In your textbook, read about nonlinear relationships on pages 17–18.
*Refer to the graph to answer questions 1–7.*

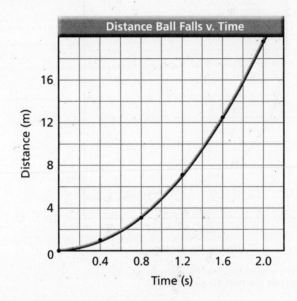

1. What sort of relationship is shown in this graph?

   _____

2. Which variable is the independent variable? Which is the dependent variable?

   _____

3. Is the slope of this graph positive or negative?

   _____

4. What are the units of the slope?

   _____

5. Explain why the slope at 2.0 s is greater than the slope at 1.0 s.

   _____

   _____

6. About how far does the ball fall in 1.8 s?

   _____

7. The equation of the graph is $d = 5t^2$. How far would the ball fall in 2.4 s?

   _____

   _____

*Refer to the graph to answer questions 8–12.*

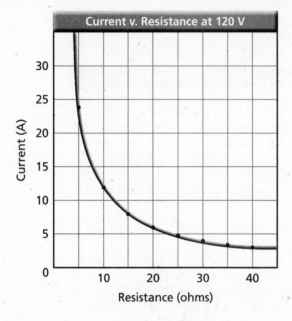

**8.** What sort of relationship is shown in this graph?

_____

**9.** Is the slope of this graph positive or negative?

_____

**10.** What are the units of the slope?

_____

**11.** What is the approximate current when the resistance is 25 ohms?

_____

**12.** Write an equation for this graph. (Hint: The equation takes the form $xy = a$, where $x$ is resistance and $y$ is current.)

_____

Read about linear and nonlinear relationships in your textbook on pages 16–18.
*For each description on the left, write the letter of the matching term on the right.*

_____ **13.** the equation of a linear relationship

_____ **14.** the shape of a graph of a linear relationship

_____ **15.** the equation of an inverse relationship

_____ **16.** the shape of the graph of an inverse relationship

_____ **17.** the equation of a quadratic relationship

_____ **18.** the shape of the graph of a quadratic relationship

**a.** hyperbola

**b.** parabola

**c.** straight line

**d.** $y = mx + b$

**e.** $y = ax^2 + bx^2 + c$

**f.** $y = \dfrac{a}{x}$

**CHAPTER**

# 1 Section 1-1 Quiz

1. Why do physicists work in SI units?

   _____

   _____

   _____

   _____

2. What are the steps in a scientific method?

   _____

   _____

   _____

3. What are significant digits? What is the role of uncertainty when using significant digits? Is zero a significant digit? Use examples to explain your answers.

   _____

   _____

   _____

   _____

   _____

   _____

   _____

   _____

   _____

   _____

4. An object with uniform acceleration a, starting from rest, will reach a speed of $v$ in time $t$ according to the formula $v = at$. How long will it take a bicyclist to go from rest to 5 m/s accelerating at 0.5 m/s$^2$?

**CHAPTER**
# 1 — Section 1-2 Quiz

**1.** What is the difference between accuracy and precision?

_____

_____

_____

_____

_____

**2.** What is the role of uncertainty in physical measurement? Give an example.

_____

_____

_____

_____

_____

**3.** Three students measured the mass of the same apple using different balances and got results of $200 \pm 20$ g, $192 \pm 10$ g, and $210 \pm 5$ g.

**a.** Which of these measurements is the most precise? Why?

_____

_____

**b.** The actual mass of the apple was 195 g. Which measurement is the most accurate?

_____

_____

**4.** A ruler has divisions of 1 mm. You use the ruler to measure a piece of paper. You find that it is 7.4 cm wide and 8.3 cm long.

**a.** What is the area of the piece of paper?



**b.** How precise were your measurements?

_____

Copyright © Glencoe/McGraw-Hill, a division of The McGraw-Hill Companies, Inc.

**CHAPTER**

# 1    Section 1-3 Quiz

1. What are the advantages of using graphs? Give an example.

   _____

   _____

   _____

   _____

   _____

   _____

2. Define the term *slope*. How do you calculate slope?

   _____

   _____

   _____

   _____

   _____

   _____

3. A line on a graph has points (3.3 mL, 6.5 g) and (5.9 mL, 4.6 g). Calculate the slope of the line.

4. The graph of a falling ball is represented by the equation $d = 7t^2 + 27$ where $d$ is in meters and $t$ is in seconds. What distance has the ball fallen after 6.00 s?

**CHAPTER**

# 1 ～ Reinforcement

### Materials

- graph paper
- ruler
- calculator

## Determining Relationships from Graphs

When data are plotted and the graph is a straight line, the relationship between the independent and dependent variables is described as a linear relationship. All such relationships can be described by the general equation $y = mx + b$. In this equation, $m$ is the slope of the line, and $b$ is the y-intercept.

### Procedure

| Time (days) | Rainfall (cm) |
|:-----------:|:-------------:|
| 0.0 | 0.0 |
| 0.5 | 1.0 |
| 1.0 | 2.6 |
| 1.5 | 4.0 |

Using the data in the table, create a graph of the amount of rainfall versus time.

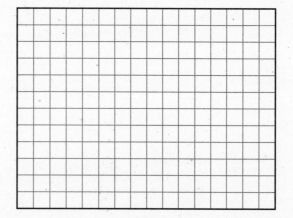

# 1   Reinforcement

## Results

1.  What is the slope of this graph?

2.  What is the $y$-intercept?

    _____

3.  What is the equation that describes the relationship shown in the graph? Include the appropriate units in your equation.

    _____

4.  Could a graph recording daily rainfall ever have a negative slope? Why or why not?

    _____

    _____

    _____

5.  In the tropics, rain falls faster than average. If recorded and graphed, how would the tropical rainfall data affect the slope of the graph.

    _____

    _____

    _____

**CHAPTER**

# 1 ___ Enrichment

---

## Materials

- graph paper
- ruler
- calculator

# Graphing Nonlinear Relationships

Seventeenth-century physicist Galileo looked for an equation to compute the distance traveled by a falling object. He created a mathematical expression relating distance ($d$), the gravitational attraction of Earth near its surface ($g$), and time ($t$):

$$d = \frac{1}{2}gt^2.$$

At Earth's surface, $g$ is a constant measuring 9.80 m/s$^2$.

## Procedure

Use Galileo's equation to create a table quantifying the distance a falling object travels every second for 10 seconds.

| Time (s) | Distance (m) |
|----------|--------------|
|          |              |
|          |              |
|          |              |
|          |              |
|          |              |
|          |              |
|          |              |
|          |              |
|          |              |
|          |              |

## Results

**1.** What is the independent variable in Galileo's equation? What is the dependent variable? Explain your answer.

_____

_____

_____

_____

**2.** Graph the results from the table on the previous page.

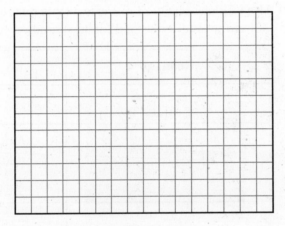

**3.** What shape is the line of best fit on your graph? Why?

_____

_____

_____

_____

## Dimensional Analysis

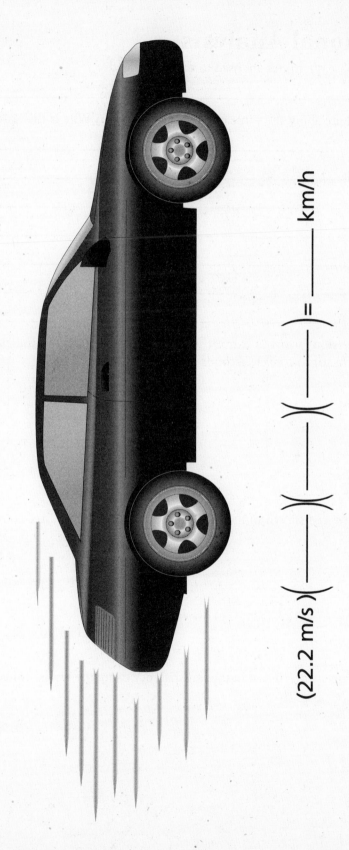

$$(22.2 \text{ m/s}) \left( \phantom{xxx} \right) \left( \phantom{xxx} \right) \left( \phantom{xxx} \right) = \underline{\phantom{xxx}} \text{ km/h}$$

## 1     Transparency 1-1 Worksheet

# Dimensional Analysis

**1.** What two base quantities are used to measure speed?

_____

**2.** What is unique about the value of a conversion factor? Why is this value important?

_____

_____

_____

_____

_____

_____

_____

**3.** Using conversion factors to convert seconds into minutes and minutes into hours, find a conversion factor to convert seconds directly into hours.

**4.** Convert the speed shown in the transparency to km/h using three conversion factors.

**5.** Make the conversion shown in the transparency using the fewest conversion factors possible.

Copyright © Glencoe/McGraw-Hill, a division of The McGraw-Hill Companies, Inc.

# A Scientific Method

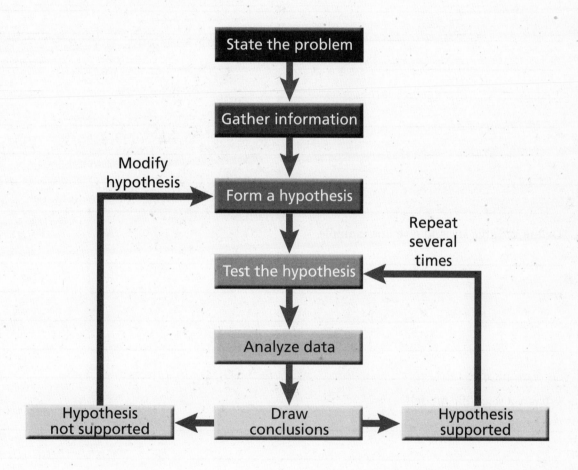

State the problem

Gather information

Modify hypothesis

Form a hypothesis

Test the hypothesis

Repeat several times

Analyze data

Hypothesis not supported

Draw conclusions

Hypothesis supported

# 1 — Transparency 1-2 Worksheet

# A Scientific Method

**1.** Why is observation crucial to the scientific process?

_____
_____
_____
_____
_____
_____
_____
_____
_____
_____

**2.** Define *scientific law* and give one example.

_____
_____
_____
_____
_____

**3.** What is a scientific model?

_____
_____
_____

**4.** What is a scientific theory? How is it different from a scientific law?

_____
_____
_____
_____
_____
_____

# Accuracy and Precision

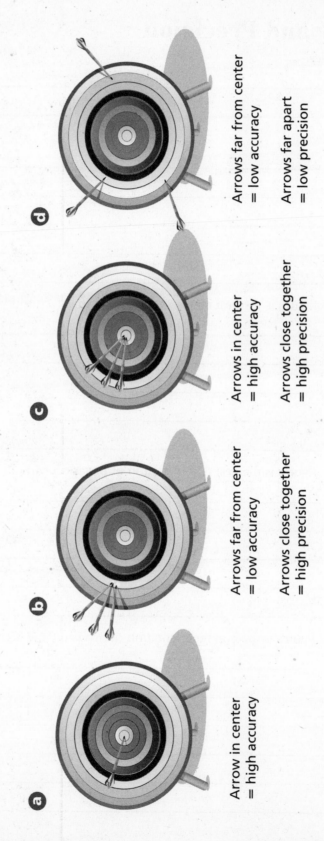

**d** Arrows far from center
= low accuracy

Arrows far apart
= low precision

**c** Arrows in center
= high accuracy

Arrows close together
= high precision

**b** Arrows far from center
= low accuracy

Arrows close together
= high precision

**a** Arrow in center
= high accuracy

# 1 Transparency 1-3 Worksheet

## Accuracy and Precision

**1.** Define *accuracy*.

_____

_____

**2.** Define *precision*.

_____

_____

_____

_____

**3.** Which of the figures is the best representation of accuracy without precision? Why?

_____

_____

_____

_____

**4.** Which of the figures is the best representation of precision without accuracy? Why?

_____

_____

_____

_____

**5.** Which of the figures is the best representation of precision and accuracy? Why?

_____

_____

_____

_____

_____

# Transparency 1-4

## Using Variables and Predicting

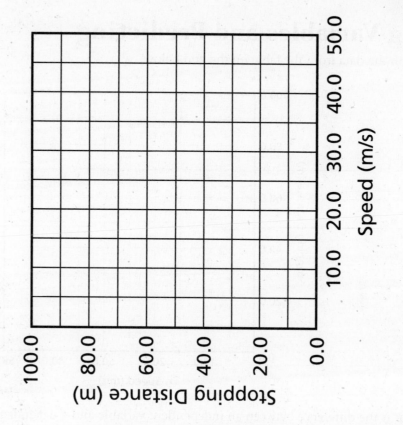

| Speed (m/s) | Stopping Distance (m) |
|---|---|
| 11.0 | 18.0 |
| 16.0 | 32.0 |
| 20.0 | 49.0 |
| 25.0 | 68.0 |
| 29.0 | 92.0 |

## 1 ⌒ Transparency 1-4 Worksheet

# Using Variables and Predicting

1.  Graph the data from the table on the grid below.

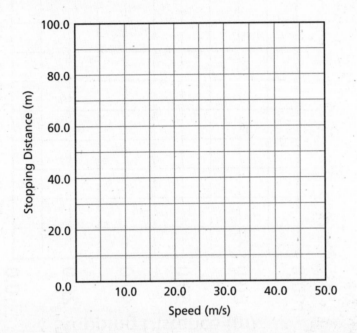

2.  What is the difference between an independent variable and a dependent variable?

_____

_____

_____

_____

3.  What are the dependent and the independent variables in the scenario shown?

_____

_____

4.  What type of relationship between speed and stopping distance is illustrated by the graph?

_____

_____

5.  As speed increases beyond 300.0 m/s, what will happen to the rate at which stopping distance changes?

_____

_____

**CHAPTER**

# 1 Chapter Assessment

# A Physics Toolkit

## Understanding Physics Concepts

*Circle the letter of the choice that best completes the statement or answers the question.*

1. The base SI unit for length is the _____.

   **a.** foot            **c.** meter

   **b.** inch            **d.** kilogram

2. The metric prefix that means $1 \times 10^6$ is _____.

   **a.** pico            **c.** nano

   **b.** mega            **d.** giga

3. To avoid parallax errors, laboratory instruments should be read _____.

   **a.** at eye level            **c.** below eye level

   **b.** from the side            **d.** at all of these positions

4. How many significant digits are in the measurement $2.560 \times 10^4$?

   **a.** 1            **c.** 3

   **b.** 2            **d.** 4

5. A sample weighs 28.40 g. Which is the estimated digit?

   **a.** 2            **c.** 4

   **b.** 8            **d.** 0

*For each of the statements below, write* true *or rewrite the italicized part to make the statement true.*

6. _____ In a scientific method, conclusions are tested to find out whether they are *valid*.

7. _____ The degree of exactness of a measurement is called *accuracy*.

8. _____ Other scientists must be able to recreate an experiment and obtain similar *data*.

9. _____ The last digit in any measurement is the *significant* digit.

10. _____ Zeros at the *end* of the number locate the decimal point.

*Answer the following questions. Use complete sentences.*

**11.** Describe the method that physicists use to study problems.

_____

_____

_____

**12.** Describe two applications that resulted from the work of physicists.

_____

_____

_____

**13.** Which of the following is a more precise measurement—the length of a tabletop measured with a stick calibrated in centimeters as shown on the left or the length measured with a stick calibrated in millimeters as shown on the right? Why?

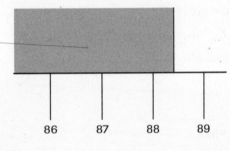 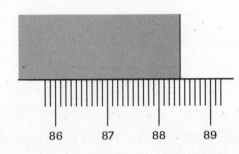

_____

_____

_____

**14.** Express the measurements in the diagram above in centimeters.

_____

**15.** How many significant digits are in each of the following measurements?

   **a.** 3809 m _____

   **b.** 9.013 m _____

   **c.** 0.0045 m _____

**16.** What is the difference between accuracy and precision?

_____

_____

_____

## Thinking Critically

*Circle the letter of the choice that best completes the statement or answers the question.*

1. The slope of a straight-line graph is the rise _____ the run.
   - **a.** added to
   - **b.** subtracted from
   - **c.** multiplied by
   - **d.** divided by

2. A _____ is the current best explanation for why things work they way they do.
   - **a.** theory
   - **b.** hypothesis
   - **c.** method
   - **d.** prediction

3. A line drawn as close as possible to all data points is called the _____.
   - **a.** linear relationship
   - **b.** line of best fit
   - **c.** vertical value
   - **d.** parabola

4. One of the scientist's most useful tools for making predictions is the _____.
   - **a.** SI unit
   - **b.** significant digit
   - **c.** graph
   - **d.** measurement

5. Which equation is most closely associated with an inverse relationship.
   - **a.** $y = mx + b$
   - **b.** $m = \dfrac{\Delta y}{\Delta x}$
   - **c.** $y = ax^2 + bx + c$
   - **d.** $y = \dfrac{a}{x}$

6. Which of the following must be included in the horizontal-axis label of a graph?
   - **a.** the graph title
   - **b.** the variable "time"
   - **c.** a unit of measurement
   - **d.** the slope

7. Which of the following is not an SI base unit?
   - **a.** meter
   - **b.** kilogram
   - **c.** kelvin
   - **d.** second

*For each of the statements below, write* true *or rewrite the italicized part to make the statement true.*

8. _____ The units used to label the answer to a physics problem may change when you *multiply or divide.*

9. _____ A graph in the shape of a parabola represents an *inverse* relationship.

10. _____ The factor that is changed or manipulated during an experiment is the *independent* variable.

11. _____ When constructing a graph from data, the range of the *x*-axis is determined by the range of the *dependent* variable.

12. _____ A graph in the shape of a hyperbola represents an *inverse* relationship.

13. _____ A straight line represents a *quadratic* relationship.

*Answer the following questions.*

**14.** Express the measurements in scientific notation.

**a.** 142000 s

_____

**b.** 0.00809 kg

_____

**c.** 501 000 000 m

_____

**15.** Simplify the following expressions. Give your answers in scientific notation, using the correct number of significant digits.

**a.** $(2\times10^6 \text{ m})(5\times10^5 \text{ m})$

_____

**b.** $\dfrac{12\times10^6 \text{ m}}{4\times10^2 \text{ s}}$

_____

**c.** $(5.06\times10^2 \text{ m}) + (8.124 \text{ km})$

_____

**16.** Describe the relationship between the variables shown in the graph below. What is the general equation that is used to represent this type of relationship?

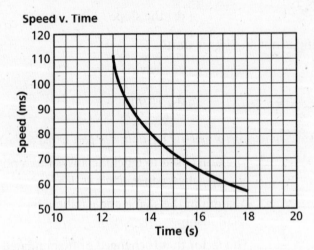

_____

_____

_____

*Physics: Principles and Problems*

## Applying Physics Knowledge

*Answer the following questions. Use complete sentences.*

1. Which of the following measurements contains zeros that are not significant? Give a reason for your answer.

   $3.050 \times 10^5$ mm          0.0053 m          45.020 cm          101.2 g

   _____

   _____

   _____

   _____

   _____

2. How are independent and dependent variables related? Identify the graph axis on which each type of variable would be plotted.

   _____

   _____

   _____

   _____

*Answer the following questions. Show your calculations.*

3. The total mass of four containers is 5.000 kg. If the mass of container A is 256 mg, container B is 5117 cg, and container C is 382 g, what is the mass of container D?

4. Show that the measurements below are equivalent.

   5687 nm, 0.000 056 87 dm

5. The results of a class experiment investigating the relationship between mass and acceleration are shown in the table below. The force applied to each mass remained constant.

| Mass (kg) | Acceleration (m/s$^2$) |
|-----------|------------------------|
| 0.5 | 6.0 |
| 1.0 | 3.0 |
| 1.5 | 2.0 |
| 2.0 | 1.5 |
| 2.5 | 1.2 |
| 3.0 | 1.0 |

   **a.** Plot the values given and draw the curve that best fits the points.

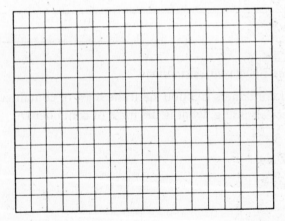

   **b.** Describe the resulting curve.

   _____

   **c.** What is the relationship between mass and the acceleration produced by a constant force?

   _____

   **d.** What is the general equation for the relationship shown in the graph?

   _____

   _____

6. Convert 86 km/h to m/s.

# Reproducible Pages Contents

## Representing Motion

CHAPTER
# 2    Mini Lab Worksheet

## Instantaneous Velocity Vectors 👓🔧

1. Attach a 1-m-long string to your hooked mass.

2. Hold the string in one hand with the mass suspended.

3. Carefully pull the mass to one side and release it.

4. **Observe** the motion, the speed, and direction of the mass for several swings.

5. Stop the mass from swinging.

6. Draw a diagram showing instantaneous velocity vectors at the following points: top of the swing, midpoint between top and bottom, bottom of the swing, midpoint between bottom and top, and back to the top of the swing.

## Analyze and Conclude

7. Where was the velocity greatest?

_____

8. Where was the velocity least?

_____

9. **Explain** how the average speed can be determined using your vector diagram.

_____

_____

_____

**CHAPTER**
# 2 — Physics Lab Worksheet

## Materials

- video camera
- two toy windup cars
- meterstick
- foam board

## Creating Motion Diagrams

In this activity you will construct motion diagrams for two toy cars. A motion diagram consists of a series of images showing the positions of a moving object at equal time intervals. Motion diagrams help describe the motion of an object. By looking at a motion diagram, you can determine whether an object is speeding up, slowing down, or moving at constant speed.

### Question

How do the motion diagrams of a fast toy car and a slow toy car differ?

### Objectives

- **Measure in SI** the location of a moving object.
- **Recognize spatial relationships** of moving objects.
- **Describe** the motion of a fast and slow object.

### Procedure

1. Mark a starting line on the lab table or the surface recommended by your teacher.

2. Place both toy cars at the starting line and release them at the same time. Be sure to wind them up before releasing them.

| Data Table 1 | |
|---|---|
| **Time (s)** | **Position of the Slower Toy Car (cm)** |
| **0.0** | |
| **0.1** | |
| **0.2** | |
| **0.3** | |
| **0.4** | |
| **0.5** | |

| Data Table 2 | |
|---|---|
| **Time (s)** | **Position of the Faster Toy Car (cm)** |
| **0.0** | |
| **0.1** | |
| **0.2** | |
| **0.3** | |
| **0.4** | |
| **0.5** | |

| Data Table 3 | |
|---|---|
| **Time (s)** | **Position of the Slower Toy Car on the Ramp (cm)** |
| **0.0** | |
| **0.1** | |
| **0.2** | |
| **0.3** | |
| **0.4** | |
| **0.5** | |

3. Observe both toy cars and determine which one is faster.

4. Place the slower toy car at the starting line.

5. Place a meterstick parallel to the path the toy car will take.

6. Have one of the members of your group get ready to operate the video camera.

7. Release the slower toy car from the starting line. Be sure to wind up the toy car before releasing it.

8. Use the video camera to record the slower toy car's motion parallel to the meterstick.

9. Set the recorder to play the tape frame-by-frame. Replay the video tape for 0.5 s, pressing the pause button every 0.1 s (3 frames).

10. Determine the toy car's position for each time interval by reading the meterstick on the video tape. Record each position in the data table.

11. Repeat steps 5–10 with the faster car.

12. Place a piece of foam board at an angle of approximately 30° to form a ramp.

13. Place the meterstick on the ramp so that it is parallel to the path the toy car will take.

14. Place the slower toy car at the top of the ramp and repeat steps 6–10.

## Analyze

1. Draw a motion diagram for the slower toy car using the data you collected.

2. Draw a motion diagram for the faster toy car using the data you collected.

3. Using the data you collected, draw a motion diagram for the slower toy car rolling down the ramp.

## Conclude and Apply

How is the motion diagram of the faster toy car different from the motion diagram of the slower toy car?

_____

_____

_____

## Going Further

1. Draw a motion diagram for a car moving at a constant speed.

**2.** What appears to be the relationship between the distances between points in the motion diagram of a car moving at a constant speed?

_____

_____

_____

**3.** Draw a motion diagram for a car that starts moving fast and then begins to slow down.

**4.** What happens to the distance between points in the motion diagram in the previous question as the car slows down?

_____

_____

_____

**5.** Draw a motion diagram for a car that starts moving slowly and then begins to speed up.

**6.** What happens to the distance between points in the motion diagram in the previous question as the car speeds up?

_____

_____

_____

## Real-World Physics

Suppose a car screeches to a halt to avoid an accident. If that car has antilock brakes that pump on and off automatically every fraction of a second, what might the tread marks on the road look like? Include a drawing along with your explanation of what the pattern of tread marks on the road might look like.

**Physics** nline

To find out more about representing motion, visit the Web site: **physicspp.com**

# CHAPTER
# 2 ⎯ Study Guide

# Representing Motion
## Vocabulary Review

*Write the term that correctly completes the statement. Use each term once.*

| | | | |
|---|---|---|---|
| average speed | instantaneous | origin | resultant |
| average velocity | position | particle model | scalar |
| coordinate system | instantaneous velocity | position | time interval |
| displacement | magnitude | position-time graph | vector |
| distance | motion diagram | | |

**1.** _____ The speed and direction of an object at a particular instant is the _____.

**2.** _____ Another term given for the size of a quantity is the _____.

**3.** _____ The _____ is the location of an object relative to an origin.

**4.** _____ The formula $t_f - t_i$ represents _____.

**5.** _____ A _____ is a quantity with both magnitude and direction.

**6.** _____ Ratio of the change in position to the time interval during which the change occurred is the _____.

**7.** _____ A system that defines the zero point of the variable you are studying is the _____.

**8.** _____ The zero point is also called the _____.

**9.** _____ A graph with time data on the horizontal axis and position data on the vertical axis is a _____.

**10.** _____ A _____ shows a series of images showing the position of a moving object over equal time intervals.

**11.** _____ A vector that represents the sum of two or more vectors is a _____.

**12.** _____ A simplified motion diagram that shows the object in motion as a series of points is a _____.

**13.** _____ A scalar quantity that is the length, or size, of the displacement vector is _____.

**14.** _____ A quantity that has only magnitude is _____.

**15.** _____ The location of an object at a particular instant is _____.

**16.** _____ The vector quantity that defines the distance and direction between two positions is _____.

**17.** _____ The absolute value of the slope on a position-time graph is _____.

### Section 2.1    Picturing Motion

In your textbook, read about motion diagrams on pages 31–33.

*Refer to the diagrams below to answer questions 1–5. Circle the letter of the choice that best completes the statement.*

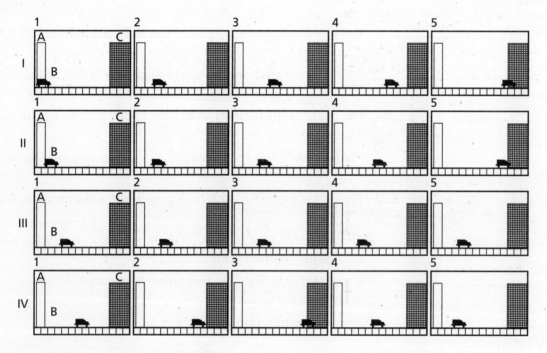

**1.** In set I, the object that is moving is _____.

   **a.** A

   **c.** C

   **b.** B

   **d.** none of the above

**2.** Set II shows that object B is _____.

   **a.** at rest

   **c.** slowing down

   **b.** increasing its speed

   **d.** traveling at a constant speed

**3.** Set _____ shows object B is slowing down.

   **a.** I

   **c.** III

   **b.** II

   **d.** IV

**4.** Set _____ shows object B at rest.

   **a.** I                               **c.** III

   **b.** II                               **d.** IV

**5.** Set _____ shows object B traveling at a constant speed.

   **a.** I                               **c.** III

   **b.** II                               **d.** IV

**Section 2.2**     # Where and When?

In your textbook, read about coordinate systems on pages 34–35.
*Refer to the diagrams below to answer questions 1–5.*

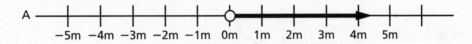

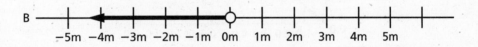

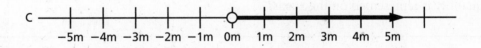

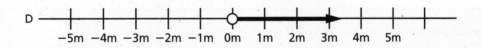

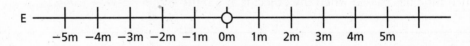

**1.** What are the position vectors for A, B, C, D, and E?

_____

**2.** If the object is moving from left to right in D, and each division represents the passage of 1 s, what is the velocity of the object?

_____

**3.** If the object is moving from right to left in D, what is the velocity of the object?

_____

**4.** In which sets are there objects with positive position vectors?

_____

**5.** In which sets are there objects with negative position vectors?

_____

**Section 2.3** **Position-Time Graphs**

*In your textbook, read about position-time graphs on pages 38–42. Refer to the diagram below to answer questions 1–7.*

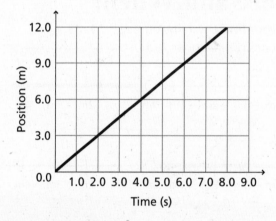

**1.** What quantity is represented on the x-axis?

_____

**2.** What quantity is represented on the y-axis?

_____

**3.** What is the position of the object at 6.0 s?

_____

**4.** How much time has passed when the object is at 6.0 m?

_____

**5.** How far does the object travel for every second it is in motion?

_____

**6.** If the object continues at this speed, when will the object reach 18.0 m?

_____

**7.** Where will the object be after 300 s?

_____

### Section 2.4   How Fast?

In your textbook, read about speed and velocity on pages 43–47.

*Refer to the diagram below to answer questions 1–12.*

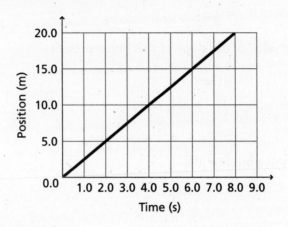

**1.** What is the formula for finding $\Delta t$?

**2.** Find $\Delta t$ for the change in position from $d = 5$ m to $d = 15$ m.

**3.** What is the formula for finding $\Delta d$?

**4.** Find $\Delta d$ for the time interval from $t = 2.0$ s to $t = 8.0$ s.

**5.** What is the formula for finding the slope on a position-time graph?

**6.** What is the slope of this line?

**7.** What does the absolute value of the slope of this line represent?

**8.** What is the velocity of this object in m/s?

**9.** If this object continues at the same velocity, how long would it take this object to reach a position of $d = 150$ m?

**10.** If this object continues at the same velocity, how far will it have traveled when $t = 200$ s?

**11.** What formula would you use to determine the position of this object if it had an initial position vector and then traveled at a fixed velocity for a certain amount of time?

**12.** How far will this object have traveled if it had an initial position of 220 m and traveled at a velocity of 2.5 m/s for 48 s?

**CHAPTER**
# 2    Section 2-1 Quiz

1. What is a motion diagram?

   _____

   _____

2. How is a particle diagram different from a motion diagram? Which diagram is simpler?

   _____

   _____

3. What are the two components used to define motion?

   _____

   _____

4. Give three examples of straight-line motion.

   _____

   _____

   _____

**CHAPTER**

# 2 Section 2-2 Quiz

1. What is the primary difference between a scalar and a vector?

_____

_____

2. What is a resultant?

_____

_____

3. A student walks 4 blocks north then stops for a rest. She then walks 9 more blocks north and rests, then finally another 6 blocks north. What is her displacement in blocks?

4. A runner runs 6 km east, 6 km north, 6 km west, and finally 6 km south. What is his total displacement? Draw a diagram. If possible, show the displacement vectors in green. Use a ruler to draw to scale.

**CHAPTER**
# 2 ___ Section 2-3 Quiz

1. On a position-time graph, which of the two variables is on the x-axis? Which is on the y-axis?

_____

_____

2. If the plotted line on a position-time graph is horizontal what does this indicate?

_____

_____

3. Can the plotted line on a position-time graph ever be vertical? Explain your answer.

_____

_____

4. A position-time graph plots the course of two runners in a race. Their lines cross on the graph.

   **a.** What does this tell you about the runners?

_____

_____

   **b.** Draw a graph as an example.

5. Does the intersecting line on a position-time graph mean that the two objects are in collision? Explain.

_____

_____

_____

**CHAPTER**
# 2 Section 2-4 Quiz

1. What is the difference between speed and velocity?

   _____

   _____

2. What is the difference between average velocity and instantaneous velocity? Give an example of each.

   _____

   _____

3. Define all three variables in the equation $v = \Delta d/\Delta t$ and indicate the appropriate label for each in SI terms.

   _____

   _____

4. What is the average velocity of a car that travels 450 km in 9.0 hours?

5. How far has a cyclist traveled if she has been moving at 30 m/s for 5.0 minutes?

# CHAPTER
## 2 — Reinforcement

## Average Velocity

Velocity is one of the more common measures you encounter each day. As you know, average velocity is the change in position (displacement) divided by the time interval during which the displacement took place. If you know two of the three quantities in this relationship, you can determine the third mathematically.

**1.** A car travels at 55 km/h for 6.0 hours. How far does it travel?

**2.** A missile travels 2500 km in 2.2 hours. What is its velocity?

**3.** How many minutes will it take a runner to finish an 11-km race at 18 km/h?

**4.** A motorcyclist travels 350 km from home on the first day of a trip. The second day he travels at 75 km/h for 8.0 hours. How far is he from home at the end of the second day?

**5.** A businesswoman on a trip flies a total of 23,000 km. The first day she traveled 4000 km, the second day 11,000 km, and on the final day she was on a plane that could travel at 570 km/h. How long was she on the plane the final day?

**CHAPTER**

# 2 ⟍ Enrichment

## Instantaneous Velocity

A car is moving across a long, straight stretch of desert where automobile companies like to test the endurance of their vehicles. The car is tested at a wide variety of velocities and distances to see how it will perform.

1. Many cars require an oil change every 4000–5000 km. If this car travels without a break for 4800 km at 120 km/h, how long will it take to simulate one full cycle of time without an oil change?

2. Some cars have a warranty that lasts for up to 150,000 km. How long would it take for the warranty to run out if the car ran constantly at 110 km/h?

3. A car is tested for 1800 km on one day, 2100 km another day, and then is driven 65 km/h for 72 hours. What is the total distance the car has traveled?

4. The odometer on a car reads 4100 km after 3 days of tests. If the car had been tested on one day for 1500 km, a second day for 1200 km, then how long was the car tested the last day if it traveled at 120 km/h while being tested?

**5.** Car A traveled 1200 km in 8.0 h. Car B traveled 1100 km in 6.5 h. Car C traveled 1300 km in 8.3 h. Which car had the highest average velocity. How long would it have taken the slowest car to travel the same distance as the fastest car?

**6.** One car tested can travel 780 km on a tank of gasoline. How long should the car be able to travel at 65 km/h before it runs out of gas? If the car has a 53-L tank, then what is the average mileage of the vehicle?

**7.** Cars Q and Z are put through an endurance test to see if they can travel at 120 km/h for 5.0 hours. Each car has a 45-L fuel tank. Car Z must stop to refuel after traveling for 4.2 hours. Car Q, however, travels for 5.4 hours before running out of gas. For each car, calculate the average kilometers traveled for each liter of gas (km/L).

**8.** Refer to the problem above. How many liters does Car Q have left in its fuel tank after traveling for five hours at 120 km/h? If you were to test-drive Car Q across a desert where there were no fuel stations available for 1200 km, how many 10-L gas cans should you have in the car to refuel along the way?

## Motion Diagrams

## 2 ◢ Transparency 2-1 Worksheet

# Motion Diagrams

**1.** What variables are shown in the motion diagram?

_____

**2.** Using variables, define $\Delta d$.

_____

**3.** What is the value of $\Delta d$ in the diagram?

_____

**4.** Using variables, define $\Delta t$.

_____

**5.** What is the value of $\Delta t$ in the diagram?

_____

**6.** What is the average velocity in the diagram?

**7.** Why is the average velocity, $v$, proportional to $\Delta d$ in the diagram?

_____

**8.** If the runner is moving at constant velocity, how long will it take her to reach the 100-m mark?

_____

# Vector Addition

## Same Direction

40 m/s

30 m/s

### Addition
40 m/s + 30 m/s = 70 m/s

70 m/s

## Opposing Directions

40 m/s

30 m/s

### Subtraction
40 m/s − 30 m/s = 10 m/s

10 m/s

# Vector Addition

1. A plane is headed north at 120 km/h and has a tailwind of 30 km/h. What is the velocity of the plane relative to the ground?

2. Draw a vector diagram of problem 1.

3. A plane is headed north at 120 km/h and has a headwind of 30 km/h. What is the velocity of the plane relative to the ground?

4. Draw a vector diagram of problem 3.

## Vector Subtraction

**A**

**B**

Vectors **A** and **B**

**A**

**−B**

**A + (−B)**

Resultant of **A** and **(−B)**

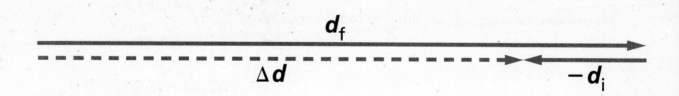

$d_f$

$\Delta d$

$-d_i$

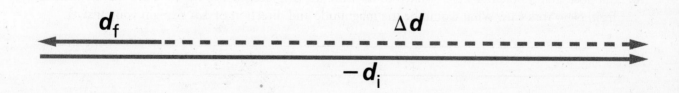

$d_f$

$\Delta d$

$-d_i$

## 2 ⬟ Transparency 2-3 Worksheet

# Vector Subtraction

1.  What is the difference between a vector and a scalar?

   _____

   _____

2.  Look at the top figure. How would you subtract vector *A* from vector *B*.

   _____

   _____

   _____

   _____

   _____

   _____

3.  Suppose the vectors in problem 2 represent the movement of a jogger. She first runs 4 km due east, then turns around and jogs 1 km due west. Describe the vector for her overall movement.

   _____

4.  Look at the bottom figure. Suppose that a car is 20 km due north of New York City. The car travels north toward Albany until it is 100 km due north of New York City.

   **a.**  What are the magnitude and direction of $d_i$?

   _____

   **b.**  What are the magnitude and direction of $d_f$?

   _____

   **c.**  Calculate the magnitude and direction of $\Delta d$.

5.  Suppose that problem 4 were restated to measure the displacement of the car from Albany instead from New York City. What would be the magnitude and direction of $\Delta d$? Explain your answer.

   _____

   _____

   _____

   _____

# Position v. Time

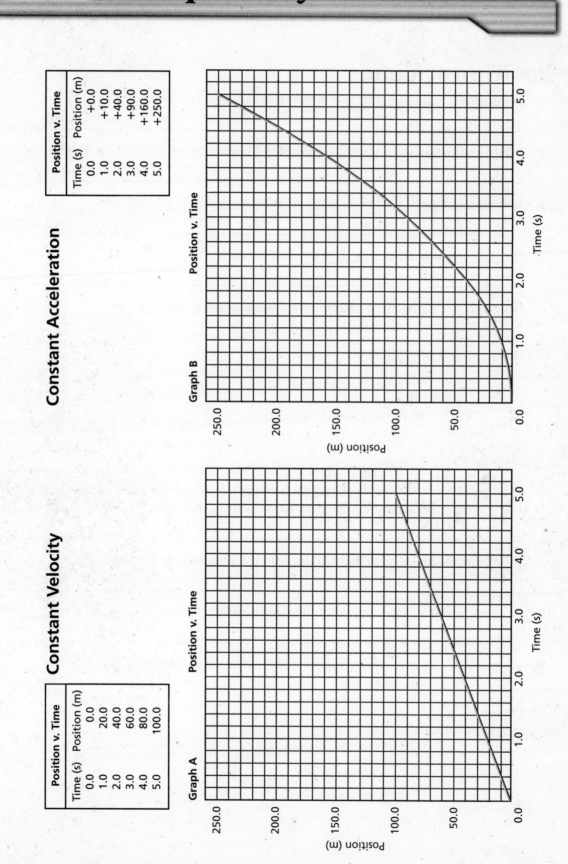

**Constant Velocity**

**Position v. Time**

| Time (s) | Position (m) |
|----------|--------------|
| 0.0 | 0.0 |
| 1.0 | 20.0 |
| 2.0 | 40.0 |
| 3.0 | 60.0 |
| 4.0 | 80.0 |
| 5.0 | 100.0 |

**Graph A** — Position v. Time

**Constant Acceleration**

**Position v. Time**

| Time (s) | Position (m) |
|----------|--------------|
| 0.0 | +0.0 |
| 1.0 | +10.0 |
| 2.0 | +40.0 |
| 3.0 | +90.0 |
| 4.0 | +160.0 |
| 5.0 | +250.0 |

**Graph B** — Position v. Time

## 2 ⬣ Transparency 2-4 Worksheet

# Position v. Time

1. On graphs A and B, what is the independent variable? The dependent variable?

   _____

2. Which graph represents a linear relationship between the variables? A parabolic relationship?

   _____

3. What is the slope of the line in graph A? What does this slope represent?

   _____

4. For graph A, what is the total displacement between 3 s and 5 s?

   _____

5. For graph A, determine the object's total displacement at 10 s.

6. For graph B, compare the displacement between 0 s and 1 s with the displacement between 1 s and 2 s. What does this indicate about the velocity of the object?

   _____

7. Compare the change in velocity of the objects represented in the two graphs.

   _____

8. At what time(s) are both objects at the same position?

   _____

9. For graph B, determine the average velocity between 0.0 s and 3.0 s.

**CHAPTER**

# 2 ～ Chapter Assessment

## Understanding Physics Concepts

*For each definition on the left, write the letter of the matching term on the right.*

_____ **1.** a system that defines the zero point of the variable you are studying

_____ **2.** the speed and direction of an object at a particular instant

_____ **3.** another term given for the size of a vector

_____ **4.** the location of an object relative to an origin

_____ **5.** $t_f - t_i$

_____ **6.** ratio of the change in position to the time interval during which the change occurred

_____ **7.** a zero point in a coordinate system

_____ **8.** a graph with time data on the horizontal axis and position data on the vertical axis

_____ **9.** a quantity with both magnitude and direction

_____ **10.** a series of images showing the position of a moving object over equal time intervals

_____ **11.** a vector that represents the sum of two or more other vectors

_____ **12.** the length of a vector that represents how far an object is from the origin

_____ **13.** a quantity that only consists of a magnitude without a direction

_____ **14.** the location of an object at a particular instant

_____ **15.** $d_f - d_i$

_____ **16.** the absolute value of the slope on a position-time graph

_____ **17.** a simplified motion diagram that shows the object in motion as a series of points

**a.** motion diagram
**b.** particle model
**c.** coordinate system
**d.** origin
**e.** position
**f.** distance
**g.** magnitude
**h.** vector
**i.** scalar
**j.** resultant
**k.** time interval
**l.** displacement
**m.** position-time graph
**n.** instantaneous position
**o.** average velocity
**p.** average speed
**q.** instantaneous velocity

*For each statement below, write* true *or rewrite the italicized part to make the statement true.*

18. _____ In the particle model, the object in motion is represented by a series of *single points*.

19. _____ A time interval is the difference between two *locations*.

20. _____ A vector has both *location* and direction.

21. _____ The zero point in a coordinate system is called the *resultant*.

22. _____ A *scalar* is a measurement that does not have a direction.

*Circle the letter of the choice that best completes the statement.*

23. In the particle model, the object in the motion diagram is replaced by _____.

    **a.** an arrow showing direction      **c.** a series of single points

    **b.** a large dot                      **d.** a scalar colored green

24. The length of the displacement vector represents how far an object _____.

    **a.** can be thrown                    **c.** traveled in one direction

    **b.** is visible                       **d.** can be stretched

25. Position-time graphs can be used to find the _____ of an object, as well as where and when two objects meet.

    **a.** velocity and position            **c.** gravity

    **b.** magnitude                        **d.** time interval

26. The average speed is _____ the average velocity.

    **a.** always slower than               **c.** the indirect value of

    **b.** the same as                      **d.** the absolute value of

27. The slope of an object's position-time graph is the _____ of the object's motion.

    **a.** distance                         **c.** average velocity

    **b.** displacement                     **d.** instantaneous velocity

28. An object's velocity is how fast it is moving and _____.

    **a.** its initial position             **c.** how far it has been

    **b.** in what direction it is moving    **d.** its instantaneous position

## Thinking Critically

*Answer the following questions. Show your calculations.*

**1.** A girl rides her bike at 15 m/s for 20 s. How far does she travel in that time?

**2.** How fast would the girl in the previous problem have been traveling if she had covered the same distance in 11 seconds?

**3.** Refer to the chart below that has data about a moving object to answer questions a–e.

| Time Elapsed | 0.0 s | 1.0 s | 2.0 s | 3.0 s | 4.0 s | 5.0 s |
| --- | --- | --- | --- | --- | --- | --- |
| Distance Traveled | 0.0 m | 10.0 m | 20.0 m | 30.0 m | 40.0 m | 80.0 m |

**a.** What is the elapsed time between the 0-m mark and the 40-m mark?

**b.** What is the average velocity of the object for the interval from 0–5 s?

**c.** How does the interval of 3–4 s compare with the interval from 4–5 s?

**d.** How does the interval of 0–4 s compare with the interval from 4–5 s?

**e.** Draw a position-time graph based on the data in the chart above.

**4.** You are planning a bicycle trip for which you want to average 24 km/h. You cover the first half of the trip at an average speed of 21 km/h. What must your average speed be in the second half of the trip to meet your goal?

**5.** You have 6.0 hours to travel a distance of 140 km by bicycle.

**a.** How long will it take you to travel the first half at an average speed of 21 km/h?

**b.** In the second half of the ride, you need to increase your average speed to make up for lost time. If you can maintain an average speed of 25 km/h, will you be able to reach your destination on time?

**c.** Show your calculations for the average speed you need to maintain in the second half of the bike ride to make up for lost time.

**d.** Draw a position-time graph for the bicycle trip. Show your position at 20-minute intervals.

# Chapter Assessment — 2

## Applying Physics Knowledge

*Answer the following questions. Use complete sentences.*

1. When viewing a scene on a VCR or DVD in frame-by-frame mode, how can you tell if an object in the frame is moving?

   _____

   _____

   _____

   _____

2. How can an object have a negative position?

   _____

   _____

   _____

3. Explain how a moving object could have a motion diagram that is the same as that of an object at rest.

   _____

   _____

   _____

   _____

4. What is meant when an object is described as having a velocity of +15 m/s?

   _____

   _____

   _____

   _____

*Solve the following problems. Show your calculations.*

5. If light travels at $3.00 \times 10^8$ m/s, how long will it take light from the sun to reach a planet that is 6.45 light years away? How far will the light have traveled in meters? (Use a value of exactly 365 days for a year.)

6. If runner A is running at 7.50 m/s and runner B is running at 7.90 m/s, how long will it take runner B to catch runner A if runner A has a 55.0-m head start?

7. A missile is fired and travels at 309 m/s. If the operator discovers that the missile is locked on the wrong target and must be detonated by remote signal before impact, how far will the missile travel if the operator's reaction time to send the signal is 1.21 s?

8. Trying to be on time for class, a girl moves at 2.4 m/s down a 52 m-long hallway, 1.2 m/s down a much more crowded hallway that is 79 m long, and the last 25 m to her class at 3.4 m/s. How long does it take her to reach her class?

9. A canoeist is trying to paddle upstream in a river that has a velocity of 6.1 m/s. If he can paddle his canoe at a velocity of 6.2 m/s will he make any headway? What will his velocity relative to the shore be?

# CHAPTER

# 3 Reproducible Pages Contents

## Accelerated Motion

## CHAPTER
# 3 ⎯ Mini Lab Worksheet

# A Steel Ball Race  👓 ✋

If two steel balls are released at the same instant, will the steel balls get closer or farther apart as they roll down a ramp?

1. **Assemble** an inclined ramp from a piece of U-channel or two metersticks taped together.

2. **Measure** 40 cm from the top of the ramp and place a mark there. Place another mark 80 cm from the top.

3. **Predict** whether the steel balls will get closer or farther apart as they roll down the ramp.

4. At the same time, release one steel ball from the top of the ramp and the other steel ball from the 40-cm mark.

5. Next, release one steel ball from the top of the ramp. As soon as it reaches the 40-cm mark, release the other steel ball from the top of the ramp.

## Analyze and Conclude

6. **Explain** your observations in terms of velocities.

   _____

   _____

   _____

7. Do the steel balls have the same velocity as they roll down the ramp? Explain.

   _____

   _____

   _____

8. Do they have the same acceleration? Explain.

   _____

   _____

   _____

**CHAPTER**
# 3 — Physics Lab Worksheet

## Materials

■ **Keep clear of falling masses.**

• spark timer

• timer tape

• 1-kg mass

• C-clamp

• stack of newspapers

• masking tape

# Acceleration Due to Gravity

Small variations in the acceleration due to gravity, $g$, occur at different places on Earth. This is because $g$ varies with distance from the center of Earth and is influenced by the subsurface geology. In addition, $g$ varies with latitude due to Earth's rotation.

For motion with constant acceleration, the displacement is $d_f - d_i = v_i(t_f - t_i) + \frac{1}{2}a(t_f - t_i)^2$. If $d_i = 0$ and $t_i = 0$, then the displacement is $d_f = v_i t_f + \frac{1}{2}at_f^2$. Dividing both sides of the equation by $t_f$ yields the following: $\frac{d_f}{t_f} = v_i + \frac{1}{2}at_f$. The slope of a graph of $\frac{d_f}{t_f}$ versus $t_f$, is equal to $\frac{1}{2}a$. The initial velocity, $v_i$, is determined by the $y$-intercept. In this activity, you will be using a spark timer to collect free-fall data and use it to determine the acceleration due to gravity, $g$.

## Question

How does the value of $g$ vary from place to place?

## Objectives

■ **Measure** free-fall data.

■ **Make and use graphs** of velocity versus time.

■ **Compare and contrast** values of $g$ for different locations.

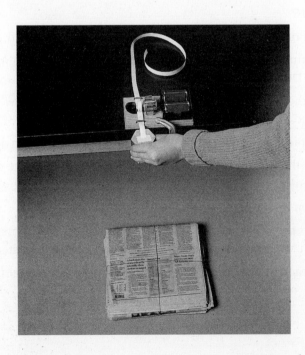

# 3 ⟋ **Physics Lab Worksheet** *continued*

| Data Table | |
|---|---|
| **Time period (#/s)** | |

| Data Table | | | |
|---|---|---|---|
| **Interval** | **Distance (cm)** | **Time (s)** | **Speed (cm/s)** |
| 1 | | | |
| 2 | | | |
| 3 | | | |
| 4 | | | |
| 5 | | | |
| 6 | | | |
| 7 | | | |
| 8 | | | |

## Procedure

1. Attach the spark timer to the edge of the lab table with the C-clamp.

2. If the timer needs to be calibrated, follow your teacher's instructions or those provided with the timer. Determine the period of the timer and record it in your data table.

3. Place the stack of newspapers on the floor, directly below the timer so that the mass, when released, will not damage the floor.

4. Cut a piece of timer tape approximately 70 cm in length and slide it into the spark timer.

5. Attach the timer tape to the 1-kg mass with a small piece of masking tape. Hold the mass next to the spark timer, over the edge of the table so that it is above the newspaper stack.

6. Turn on the spark timer and release the mass.

7. Inspect the timer tape to make sure that there are dots marked on it and that there are no gaps in the dot sequence. If your timer tape is defective, repeat steps 4–6 with another piece of timer tape.

8. Have each member of your group perform the experiment and collect his or her own data.

*Physics: Principles and Problems*

9. Choose a dot near the beginning of the timer tape, a few centimeters from the point where the timer began to record dots, and label it *0*. Label the dots after that *1, 2, 3, 4, 5*, etc. until you get near the end where the mass is no longer in free fall. If the dots stop, or the distance between them begins to get smaller, the mass is no longer in free fall.

10. Measure the total distance to each numbered dot from the zero dot to the nearest millimeter and record it in your data table. Using the timer period, record the total time associated with each distance measurement and record it in your data table.

## Analyze

1. **Use Numbers** Calculate the values for speed and record them in the data table.

2. **Make and Use Graphs** Draw a graph of speed versus time. Draw the best-fit straight line for your data.

3. Calculate the slope of the line. Convert your result to m/s$^2$.

## Conclude and Apply

1. Recall that the slope is equal to $\frac{1}{2}a$. What is the acceleration due to gravity?

2. Find the relative error for your experimental value of *g* by comparing it to the accepted value.

$$\text{Relative error} = \frac{\text{Accepted value} - \text{Experimental value}}{\text{Accepted value}} \times 100$$

**3.** What was the mass's velocity, $v_i$, when you began measuring distance and time?

## Going Further

What is the advantage of measuring several centimeters away from the beginning of the timer tape rather than from the very first dot?

_____

_____

_____

## Real-World Physics

Why do designers of free-fall amusement-park rides design exit tracks that gradually curve toward the ground? Why is there a stretch of straight track?

_____

_____

_____

## Share Your Data

**Communicate** the average value of $g$ to others. Go to **physicspp.com/internet_lab** and post the name of your school, city, state, elevation above sea level, and average value of $g$ for your class. Obtain a map for your state and a map of the United States. Using the data posted on the Web site by other students, mark the values for $g$ at the appropriate locations on the maps. Do you notice any variation in the acceleration due to gravity for different locations, regions and elevations?

_____

_____

_____

**Physics nline**

To find out more about accelerated motion, visit the Web site: **physicspp.com**

**CHAPTER**

# 3 ⬭ Study Guide

## Accelerated Motion

### Vocabulary Review

*Write the term that correctly completes the statement. Use each term once.*

acceleration                average acceleration            instantaneous acceleration

acceleration due to gravity   free fall                       velocity-time graph

**1.** _____ A _____ shows how velocity is related to time.

**2.** _____ The change in velocity of an object at an instant of time is its _____.

**3.** _____ The rate at which an object's velocity changes is its _____.

**4.** _____ The motion of falling objects when air resistance is negligible is called _____.

**5.** _____ The _____ of an object is the change in velocity during some measurable time interval divided by that time interval.

**6.** _____ The acceleration of an object in free fall that results from the influence of Earth's gravity is _____.

## Section 3.1 ⬤ Acceleration

In your textbook, read about changing velocity and velocity-time graphs on pages 58–59.

**1.** Refer to this velocity-time graph of a jogger to complete the two tables on the next page.

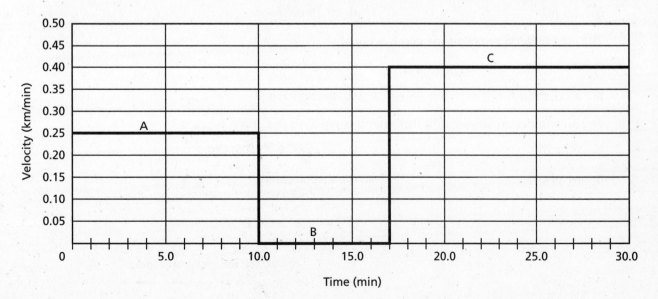

| Segment | V | Δt | Δd |
|---|---|---|---|
| A | | | |
| B | | | |
| C | | | |

| Δt | Distance Run | Displacement | Average Velocity |
|---|---|---|---|
| | | | |

In your textbook, read about acceleration on pages 59–64.

*Circle the letter of the choice that best completes the statement or answers the question.*

**2.** The slope of a tangent line on a velocity-time graph is the _____.

   **a.** displacement            **c.** average acceleration

   **b.** velocity                   **d.** acceleration due to gravity

**3.** When acceleration and velocity vectors are pointing in opposite directions, the object is _____.

   **a.** speeding up             **c.** moving at constant speed

   **b.** slowing down           **d.** not moving

**4.** If a runner accelerates from 2 m/s to 3 m/s in 4 s, her average acceleration is _____.

   **a.** $4.0 \text{ m/s}^2$           **c.** $0.40 \text{ m/s}^2$

   **b.** $2.5 \text{ m/s}^2$           **d.** $0.25 \text{ m/s}^2$

**5.** The area under a velocity-time graph is equal to the object's _____.

   **a.** stop time               **c.** displacement

   **b.** acceleration           **d.** average speed

**6.** The area under an acceleration-time graph is equal to the object's _____.

   **a.** velocity                **c.** change in acceleration

   **b.** weight                 **d.** displacement

The graph below shows the motion of five objects. Refer to the graph to answer questions 7–11.

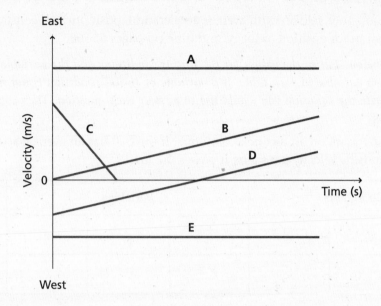

**7.** Which has the greater acceleration, Object A or B? How do you know?

_____

_____

**8.** Which of these objects has the least value of acceleration? How do you know?

_____

_____

**9.** Which of these objects started its motion from rest? Which object comes to a complete stop? Explain your answers.

_____

_____

**10.** Object D crosses the axis while maintaining a constant positive acceleration. What does this indicate?

_____

_____

_____

**11.** Object A and Object E both have a constant velocity and acceleration of zero. What is different between these two?

_____

_____

_____

**Section 3.2** **Motion with Constant Acceleration**

In your textbook, read about velocity with average acceleration, position with constant acceleration, and an alternative expression for position, velocity, and time on pages 65–68.

*Complete the tables below. Fill in the values for the initial conditions and the variables. Write a question mark for the unknown variable in each table. If a variable or initial condition is not needed to answer the problem, write X. Write the equation you would use to answer each question. Then solve the problem and show your calculations.*

1. A ball rolls past a mark on an incline at 0.40 m/s. If the ball has an average acceleration of 0.20 m/s$^2$, what is its velocity 3.0 s after it passes the mark?

| Initial Conditions | | | Variables | | | Equation |
|---|---|---|---|---|---|---|
| $\Delta t$ | $d_f$ | $v_f$ | $\bar{a}$ | $d_i$ | $v_i$ | |
| | | | | | | |

2. A car initially traveling at 15 m/s accelerates at a constant rate of 4.5 m/s$^2$ over a distance of 45 m. How long does it take the car to cover this distance?

| Initial Conditions | | | Variables | | | Equation |
|---|---|---|---|---|---|---|
| $t_f$ | $d_f$ | $v_f$ | $\bar{a}$ | $d_i$ | $v_i$ | |
| | | | | | | |

3. A car accelerates from 10.0 m/s to 15.0 m/s in 3.0 s. How far does the car travel?

| Initial Conditions | | | Variables | | | Equation |
|---|---|---|---|---|---|---|
| $t_f$ | $d_f$ | $v_f$ | $\bar{a}$ | $d_i$ | $v_i$ | |
| | | | | | | |

**4.** A race car accelerates at 4.5 m/s² from rest. What is the car's velocity after it has traveled 35.0 m?

| Initial Conditions | | | Variables | | | Equation |
|---|---|---|---|---|---|---|
| $\Delta t$ | $d_f$ | $v_f$ | $\bar{a}$ | $d_i$ | $v_i$ | |
| | | | | | | |

**Section 3.3** **Free Fall**

In your textbook, read about acceleration due to gravity on pages 72–75.

*For each statement below, write* **true** *or rewrite the italicized part to make the statement true.*

**1.** _____ A feather does not fall in the same way as a pebble because of *gravity*.

**2.** _____ *Freefall* is the motion of a falling object when the air resistance is negligible.

**3.** _____ Galileo concluded that objects in free fall have *different* accelerations.

**4.** _____ Acceleration due to gravity is *the same* for objects of different sizes.

**5.** _____ Acceleration due to gravity is always *downward*.

**6.** _____ If you drop a rock, its velocity after 3 s will be *19.6 m/s*.

**7.** _____ The decision to treat acceleration due to gravity as positive or negative depends on the *coordinate system* you use.

**8.** _____ If you toss a ball up, it reaches its maximum height when its velocity is *zero*.

**9.** _____ If you toss a ball up, its acceleration at its maximum height is *zero*.

**10.** _____ If a tossed ball had no velocity or acceleration, it would *have no motion at all*.

The diagram below shows the positions of a ball that was thrown upward at time $t_1$. Refer to the diagram to answer questions 11–14.

○ $t_2$

○ $t_3$

○ $t_1$

○ $t_4$

○ $t_0$

11. Assume that the downward direction is positive. For each time shown on the diagram, determine whether the direction of the velocity is positive, negative, or zero, and whether the direction of the acceleration is positive, negative, or zero. Record your answers in the table using the symbols +, −, and 0.

| Variable | Time | | | | |
|---|---|---|---|---|---|
| | $t_1$ | $t_2$ | $t_3$ | $t_4$ | $t_5$ |
| $v$ | | | | | |
| $a$ | | | | | |

12. Still assuming that the downward direction is positive, rank the magnitudes of the velocities $v_1$, $v_2$, $v_3$, $v_4$, $v_5$ in decreasing order.

_____

13. Now assume that the downward direction is negative. For each time shown on the diagram, determine whether the direction of the velocity is positive, negative, or zero, and whether the direction of the acceleration is positive, negative, or zero. Record your answers in the table using the symbols +, −, and 0.

| Variable | Time | | | | |
|---|---|---|---|---|---|
| | $t_1$ | $t_2$ | $t_3$ | $t_4$ | $t_5$ |
| $v$ | | | | | |
| $a$ | | | | | |

14. Still assuming that the downward direction is negative, rank the magnitudes of the velocities $v_1$, $v_2$, $v_3$, $v_4$, $v_5$ in decreasing order.

_____

**CHAPTER**

# 3 Section 3-1 Quiz

1. What is the difference between average acceleration and instantaneous acceleration?

   _____

   _____

   _____

2. If you look at a motion diagram, how can you tell whether an object is speeding up or slowing down?

   _____

   _____

   _____

3. How can you determine acceleration from a velocity-time graph?

   _____

   _____

   _____

4. A car brakes from 25 m/s to 16 m/s in 2.0 s. What is its acceleration?

5. A tangent line drawn on a velocity-time graph has a rise of 19 m/s and a run of 4.0 m/s. What is the acceleration? What type of acceleration is this?

**CHAPTER**

# 3 Section 3-2 Quiz

1. Can a position-time graph be created from a velocity-time graph? Why or why not?

   _____

   _____

   _____

2. What information can you determine from a velocity-time graph? How?

   _____

   _____

   _____

3. A cyclist traveling at 5.0 m/s accelerates with an average acceleration of 1.5 m/s$^2$ for 5.2 s. What is her final velocity?

4. A car traveling 11.00 m/s passes a marker reading 15 km. The car then accelerates with an average acceleration of 0.10 m/s$^2$ for 1 min. At approximately what marker is the car after 1.0 min?

5. A train traveling at 6.4 m/s accelerates at 0.10 m/s$^2$ over a distance of 100 m. What is its final velocity?

**CHAPTER**

# 3    Section 3-3 Quiz

1. On what does the value of *g* depend? What factors do not affect it?

 

 

 

2. How do you determine what sign to associate with *g* when using it in an equation?

 

 

 

3. If you drop a feather and a tennis ball, the feather falls slower than the ball. If free-fall acceleration is the same for all objects, why do these objects fall at different rates?

 

 

 

4. A ball is thrown upward at 49 m/s. When does it reach its highest point?

 

5. How far did the ball in Question 4 rise?

**CHAPTER**

# 3  Reinforcement

## Motion Diagrams

*Answering the following questions. Show all movement from left to right.*

1. Draw a motion diagram showing a jogger standing still. If appropriate, include vectors showing velocity and acceleration.

2. Draw a motion diagram showing a jogger moving at constant speed. If appropriate, include vectors showing velocity and acceleration.

3. Draw a motion diagram showing a jogger speeding up. If appropriate, include vectors showing velocity and acceleration.

4. Draw a motion diagram showing a jogger slowing down. If appropriate, include vectors showing velocity and acceleration.

**CHAPTER**

# 3 ~~~~ Enrichment

## Measuring Acceleration

You have felt acceleration and its effects many times. For example, acceleration pushes you back into your seat when the driver of a car speeds up. While you can feel acceleration, the sensations you feel are too subjective to measure. To measure acceleration, scientists use an instrument called an *accelerometer*.

The diagram below shows three elevators and three accelerometers. Each elevator has an accelerometer bolted to its floor. Remember that acceleration can be described as a change in velocity.

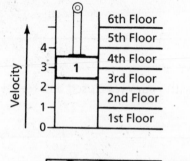

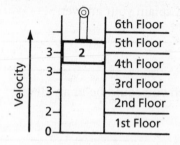

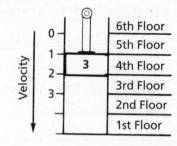

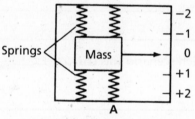

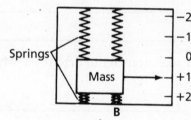

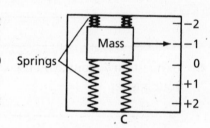

1. Which accelerometer is measuring the acceleration of Elevator A in motion between the 3rd and 4th floors? How do you know?

   _____

   _____

2. Which accelerometer is measuring the acceleration of Elevator C in motion between the 4th and 5th floors? How do you know?

   _____

   _____

3. Which accelerometer is measuring the acceleration of Elevator B in motion between the 4th and 5th floors? How do you know?

   _____

   _____

**4.** Under what conditions other than those in question 3 might an accelerometer read zero?

_____

_____

**5.** Which accelerometer most closely resembles the accelerometer in an elevator if the elevator cable were to snap? Explain your answer.

_____

_____

**6.** Which accelerometer most closely resembles the accelerometer in an elevator that was traveling upward and suddenly stopped? Explain your answer.

_____

_____

**7.** Describe three scenarios in which you could be in an elevator with your eyes closed and feel as if you were not moving.

_____

_____

_____

**8.** In question 7, could you use an accelerometer to determine which scenario was correct? Explain your answer.

_____

_____

_____

**9.** When Elevator C is taking on passengers at the 6th floor, which accelerometer would describe its situation? Explain you answer.

_____

_____

_____

**10.** Would it be possible for an elevator to show the accelerometer reading of accelerometer B but have zero velocity? If so, how?

_____

_____

_____

# Velocity v. Time

## Table A

**Velocity v. Time**

| Time (s) | Velocity (m/s) |
|----------|----------------|
| 0.0 | 150.0 |
| 1.0 | 150.0 |
| 2.0 | 150.0 |
| 3.0 | 150.0 |
| 4.0 | 150.0 |
| 5.0 | 150.0 |

## Table B

**Velocity v. Time**

| Time (s) | Velocity (m/s) |
|----------|----------------|
| 0.0 | +0.0 |
| 1.0 | +20.0 |
| 2.0 | +40.0 |
| 3.0 | +60.0 |
| 4.0 | +80.0 |
| 5.0 | +100.0 |

**Graph A**
**Velocity v. Time**

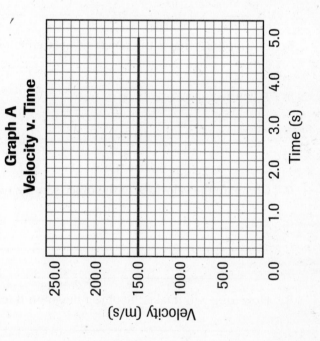

**Graph B**
**Velocity v. Time**

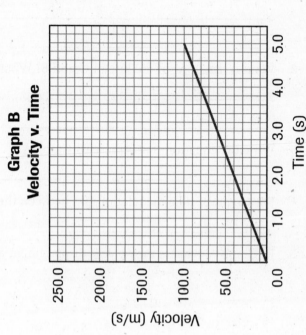

# 3 ⬡ **Transparency 3-1 Worksheet**

# Velocity v. Time

**1.** In which graph is the object moving at a constant velocity? What is the velocity?

_____

_____

**2.** What is the slope of the line in Graph B? What value does the slope represent?

_____

_____

**3.** Write the equation that represents Graph A.

_____

**4.** For Graph B, state the relationship between the variables as an equation.

_____

**5.** In Graph A, what is the object's displacement at 4.5 s?

**6.** In Graph B, what is the object's displacement between 2.0 s and 5.0 s?

**7.** Compare the velocities of the objects in the two graphs at 3.0 s.

_____

_____

_____

**8.** How long will it take the object in Graph B to reach the velocity of the object in Graph A?

_____

**9.** What is the difference in velocity between the two objects at 2.0 s?

_____

*Physics: Principles and Problems*

# Positive and Negative Acceleration

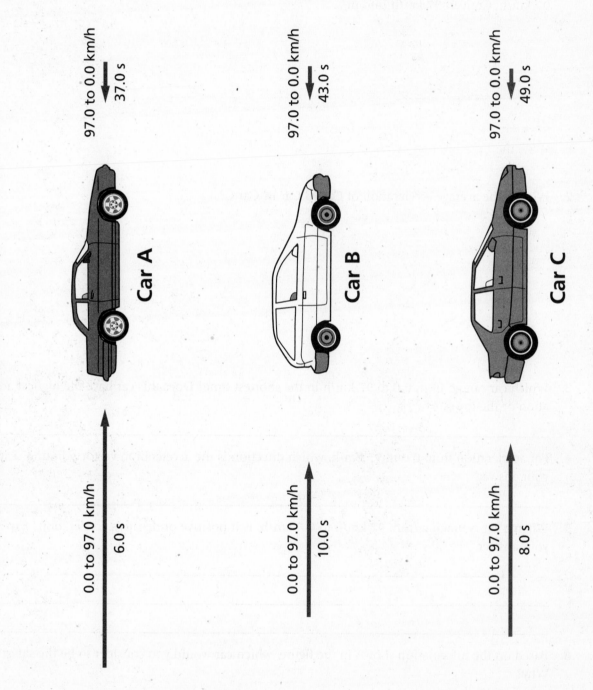

0.0 to 97.0 km/h

6.0 s

97.0 to 0.0 km/h

37.0 s

Car A

0.0 to 97.0 km/h

10.0 s

97.0 to 0.0 km/h

43.0 s

Car B

0.0 to 97.0 km/h

8.0 s

97.0 to 0.0 km/h

49.0 s

Car C

Date ______________ Period ______________ Name ______________________

# 3 Transparency 3-2 Worksheet

## Positive and Negative Acceleration

1. Acceleration figures for cars usually are given as the number of seconds needed to go from 0.0 to 97 km/h. Convert 97 km/h into m/s.

2. What is the average acceleration of Car A? Car B? Car C?

3. Which car can go from 0.0 to 97 km/h in the shortest time? Does this car have the highest acceleration or the lowest?

______________________________________________

4. For acceleration from 0.0 to 97 km/h, which direction is the acceleration vector pointing? Explain your answer.

______________________________________________

5. When a car is braking from 97 km/h to 0.0 km/h, is it positive or negative acceleration? Explain your answer.

______________________________________________

______________________________________________

______________________________________________

6. Based on the information shown in the figure, which car would you consider to be the safest? Why?

______________________________________________

______________________________________________

# Position, Velocity, and Acceleration

### Time v. Position

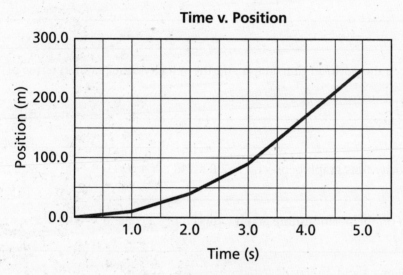

| Time (s) | Position (m) |
|----------|--------------|
| 0.0 | 0.0 |
| 1.0 | 10.0 |
| 2.0 | 40.0 |
| 3.0 | 90.0 |
| 4.0 | 160.0 |
| 5.0 | 250.0 |

### Time v. Velocity

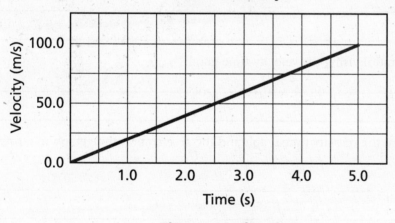

| Time (s) | Velocity (m/s) |
|----------|----------------|
| 0.0 | 0.0 |
| 1.0 | 20.0 |
| 2.0 | 40.0 |
| 3.0 | 60.0 |
| 4.0 | 80.0 |
| 5.0 | 100.0 |

### Time v. Acceleration

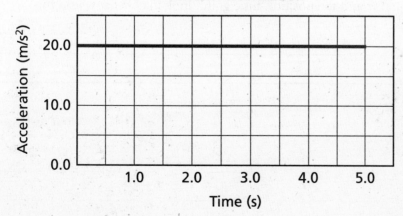

| Time (s) | Acceleration (m/s$^2$) |
|----------|------------------------|
| 0.0 | 20.0 |
| 1.0 | 20.0 |
| 2.0 | 20.0 |
| 3.0 | 20.0 |
| 4.0 | 20.0 |
| 5.0 | 20.0 |

# 3 ⎯ Transparency 3-3 Worksheet

# Position, Velocity, and Acceleration

1. How can you determine velocity using the position-time graph?

   _____

   _____

2. What is the relationship between the position-time graph and the velocity-time graph in terms of velocity?

   _____

   _____

3. What is the area under the velocity-time graph between $t = 2.0$ s and $t = 4.0$ s?

   _____

4. What is the change in position on the position-time graph between $t = 2.0$ s and $t = 4.0$ s?

   _____

5. How are your answers to problems 3 and 4 related?

   _____

   _____

6. How can you determine acceleration using the velocity-time graph?

   _____

   _____

7. How is the relationship between the velocity-time graph and the acceleration-time graph in terms of acceleration?

   _____

   _____

8. If the velocity were constant, what would the position-time graph look like? What would the acceleration-time graph look like?

   _____

   _____

# Free Fall on the Moon

**Earth**

$g = 9.80$ m/s$^2$

$v = 4.90$ m/s

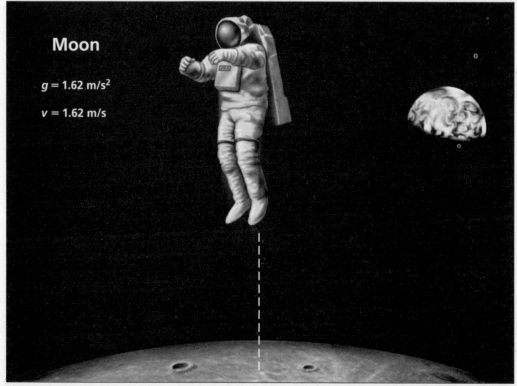

**Moon**

$g = 1.62$ m/s$^2$

$v = 1.62$ m/s

# 3 ⬡ Transparency 3-4 Worksheet

# Free Fall on the Moon

**1.** A boy on Earth jumps straight upward with an initial velocity of 4.9 m/s.

   **a.** How long does it take for him to reach maximum height?

   **b.** At maximum height, what is his velocity?

   **c.** At maximum height, what is his acceleration? Explain your answer.

   _____

   _____

   _____

**2.** An astronaut wearing a 20-kg spacesuit jumps on the Moon with an initial velocity of 16 m/s. On the Moon, the acceleration due to gravity is 1.62 m/s$^2$. (Assume that downward is the positive direction.)

   **a.** How long does it take him to reach maximum height?

   **b.** What is the maximum height he reaches?

   **c.** If you drew a velocity-time graph for the motion of the astronaut, what would be the slope of the line?

   **d.** Are the vectors for acceleration and initial velocity pointed in the same or different directions? Explain your answer.

   _____

   _____

**CHAPTER**

# 3 — Chapter Assessment

## Accelerated Motion

### Understanding Physics Concepts

*For each description on the left, write the letter of the matching term on the right.*

_____ **1.** the motion of a falling object when air resistance is negligible

_____ **2.** the change in velocity of an object at an instant of time

_____ **3.** the acceleration of an object in free fall that results from the influence of Earth's gravity

_____ **4.** the rate at which an object's velocity changes

_____ **5.** the change in velocity of an object during some measurable time interval divided by that time interval

_____ **6.** a graph that shows how velocity is related to time

**a.** acceleration

**b.** instantaneous acceleration

**c.** velocity-time graph

**d.** acceleration due to gravity

**e.** free fall

**f.** average acceleration

*For each statement below, write* true *or rewrite the italicized part to make the statement true.*

**7.** _____ Velocity-time graphs can be used to find the velocity and *position* of an object.

**8.** _____ Acceleration vectors show the magnitude and *direction* of the average acceleration during a time interval.

**9.** _____ When the vectors for acceleration and velocity are pointing in opposite directions, an object is *speeding up*.

**10.** _____ When a child drops a ball, the instantaneous velocity of the ball as the child lets go is *zero*.

**11.** _____ When a child drops a ball, the instantaneous acceleration of the ball as the child lets go is *zero*.

**12.** _____ A toy rocket is launched vertically upward. When the rocket reaches its highest point, its velocity is *at its maximum*.

**13.** _____ The acceleration due to gravity on Earth, *g*, is 9.80 m/s² *in any direction*.

**14.** _____ You can use equations for motion with *constant acceleration* to solve problems involving objects in free fall.

*Circle the letter of the choice that best completes the statement or answers the question.*

**15.** If you close your eyes and feel as if you are not moving, you may be experiencing _____.

    **a.** nonuniform motion         **c.** uniform motion

    **b.** acceleration         **d.** circular motion

**16.** The _____ is not shown on a motion diagram.

    **a.** acceleration of an object         **c.** velocity of an object

    **b.** exact location of an object         **d.** distance between successive positions of an object

**17.** Changing velocity on a motion diagram is shown using _____.

    **a.** a varying time scale         **c.** the length of the acceleration vectors

    **b.** scalar values of the position         **d.** the length of the velocity vectors

**18.** Which of the following results in the largest acceleration?

    **a.** a small change in velocity over a short time interval

    **b.** a large change in velocity over a short time interval

    **c.** a small change in velocity over a long time interval

    **d.** a large change in velocity over a long time interval

**19.** Average acceleration is the same as instantaneous acceleration when _____.

    **a.** acceleration is constant         **c.** velocity is constant

    **b.** acceleration is changing         **d.** a velocity-time graph can be drawn

**20.** As velocity increases, an object's displacement _____.

    **a.** cannot be determined         **c.** decreases for each time interval

    **b.** remains the same for each         **d.** increases for each time interval
       time interval

**21.** The area under a velocity-time graph is equal to the object's _____.

    **a.** acceleration         **c.** time of travel

    **b.** instantaneous velocity         **d.** displacement

**22.** In a strobe photo of a dropped egg, the displacement between each pair of images increases. This shows that _____.

    **a.** the velocity is increasing         **c.** the acceleration is increasing

    **b.** the velocity is decreasing         **d.** the velocity is constant

**23.** A constant net force acts on an object. Describe the motion of the object.

    **a.** increasing acceleration         **c.** constant acceleration

    **b.** constant velocity         **d.** constant speed

## Thinking Critically

1. A skateboarder starts from rest and maintains a constant acceleration of 0.50 m/s$^2$ for 8.4 s. What is the rider's displacement during this time?

2. A sports car can move 100.0 m in the first 4.5 s of constant acceleration.

   **a.** What is the car's acceleration?

   **b.** Draw a velocity-time graph with the slope of a car moving with constant acceleration.

3. A rolling ball has an initial velocity of 1.6 m/s.

   **a.** If the ball has a constant acceleration of 0.33 m/s$^2$, what is its velocity after 3.6 s?

   **b.** How far did the ball travel?

**4.** Use the data table below to create a velocity-time graph.

| Time (s) | Velocity (m/s) | Time (s) | Velocity (m/s) |
|----------|----------------|----------|----------------|
| 0.0 | 20.0 | 7.0 | 33.0 |
| 2.0 | 20.0 | 8.0 | 40.0 |
| 4.0 | 20.0 | 10.0 | 25.0 |
| 5.0 | 20.0 | 11.0 | 17.5 |
| 6.0 | 26.0 | 12.0 | 10.0 |

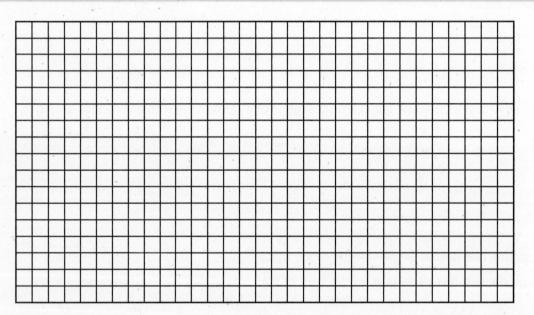

**5.** Refer to the graph you created and describe the velocity and the acceleration of the object in question 4.

_____

_____

_____

_____

_____

## Applying Physics Knowledge

**1.** After making a delivery, a truck driver must maneuver the vehicle backward down a narrow ramp. The speed of the truck increases with distance down the ramp. Describe the truck's acceleration.

_____

_____

_____

_____

**2.** What is the instantaneous acceleration of an object whose motion on a velocity-time graph is represented as a straight line?

_____

_____

**3.** Suppose an object starts from rest and has a constant acceleration. How can you determine the displacement of the object from a velocity-time graph.

_____

_____

_____

**4.** How is the acceleration of an object in free fall related to the acceleration due to gravity?

_____

_____

**5.** A toy rocket is shot straight up into the air with an initial speed of 45.0 m/s.

   **a.** How long does it take for the rocket to reach its highest point?

   **b.** How high does the rocket rise above the ground?

**6.** A squirrel drops an acorn from a tree branch that is 8.00 m from the ground.

   **a.** How long is the acorn in the air?

   **b.** What is the acorn's velocity when it reaches the ground?

   **c.** Draw a velocity-time graph. Shade the area that shows the acorn's displacement.

# Reproducible Pages Contents

## Forces in One Dimension

**CHAPTER**

# 4 ~~ Mini Lab Worksheet

## Tug-of-War Challenge 👓🔨

In a tug-of-war, predict how the force you exert on your end of the rope compares to the force your opponent exerts if you pull and your opponent just holds the rope.

**1. Predict** how the forces compare if the rope moves in your direction.

_____

_____

**2. Test** your prediction. *CAUTION: Do not suddenly let go of the rope.*

## Analyze and Conclude

**3. Compare** the force on your end of the rope to the force on your opponent's end of the rope. What happened when you started to move your opponent's direction?

_____

_____

_____

_____

**CHAPTER**

# 4 ~~~ Physics Lab Worksheet

## Materials

- **Use caution when working around elevator doors.**

- **Do not interfere with normal elevator traffic.**

- **Watch that the mass on the spring scale does not fall and hit someone's feet or toes.**

- elevator

- bathroom scale

- spring scale

- mass

## Forces in an Elevator

Have you ever been in a fast-moving elevator? Was the ride comfortable? How about an amusement ride that quickly moves upward or one that free-falls? What forces are acting on you during your ride? In this experiment, you will investigate the forces that affect you during vertical motion when gravity is involved with a bathroom scale. Many bathroom scales measure weight in pounds mass (lbm) or pounds force (lbf) rather than newtons. In the experiment, you will need to convert weights measured on common household bathroom scales to SI units.

## Question

What one-dimensional forces act on an object that is moving in a vertical direction in relation to the ground?

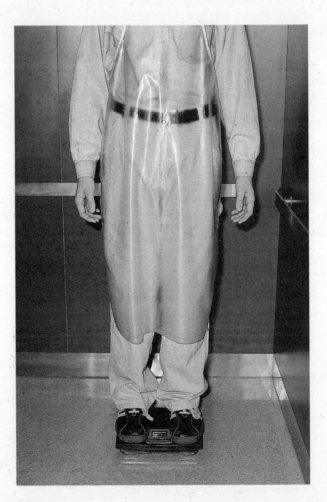

| Data Table | |
|---|---|
| **Force (step 1)** | |
| **Highest Reading (step 2)** | |
| **Reading at Constant Velocity (step 2)** | |
| **Lowest Reading (step 2)** | |
| **Your Weight (step 3)** | |
| **Highest Reading (step 4)** | |
| **Reading at Constant Velocity (step 5)** | |
| **Lowest Reading (step 6)** | |

## Objectives

- **Measure** Examine forces that act on objects that move vertically.
- **Compare and Contrast** Differentiate between actual weight and apparent weight.
- **Analyze and Conclude** Share and compare data of the acceleration of elevators.

## Procedure

1. Securely attach a mass to the hook on a spring scale. Record the force of the mass in the data table.

2. Accelerate the mass upward, then move it upward at a constant velocity, and then slow the mass down. Record the greatest amount of force on the scale, the amount of force at constant velocity, and the lowest scale reading.

3. Get your teacher's permission and proceed to an elevator on the ground floor. Before entering the elevator, measure your weight on a bathroom scale. Record this weight in the data table.

4. Place the scale in the elevator. Step on the scale and record the mass at rest. Select the highest floor that the elevator goes up to. Once the elevator starts, during its upward acceleration, record the highest reading on the scale in the data table.

5. When the velocity of the elevator becomes constant, record the reading on the scale in the data table.

6. As the elevator starts to decelerate, watch for the lowest reading on the scale and record it in the data table.

## Analyze

1. **Explain** In step 2, why did the mass appear to gain weight when being accelerated upward? Provide a mathematical equation to summarize this concept.

2. **Explain** Why did the mass appear to lose weight when being decelerated at the end of its movement during step 3? Provide a mathematical equation to summarize this concept.

3. **Measure in SI** Most bathroom scales read in pounds mass (lbm). Convert your reading in step 4 in pounds mass to kilograms. (1 kg = 2.21 lbm) (Note: skip this step if your scale measures in kilograms.)

4. **Measure in SI** Some bathroom scales read in pounds force (lbf). Convert all of the readings you made in steps 4–6 to newtons. (1 N = 0.225 lbf)

5. **Analyze** Calculate the acceleration of the elevator at the beginning of your elevator trip using the equation $F_{scale} = ma + mg$.

6. **Use Numbers** What is the acceleration of the elevator at the end of your trip?

## Conclude and Apply

How can you develop an experiment to find the acceleration of an amusement park ride that either drops rapidly or climbs rapidly?

_____

_____

_____

## Going Further

How can a bathroom scale measure both pounds mass (lbm) and pounds force (lbf) at the same time?

_____

_____

_____

## Real-World Physics

Forces on pilots in high-performance jet airplanes are measured in *g*'s or *g*-force. What does it mean if a pilot is pulling 6 *g*'s in a power climb?

_____

_____

_____

## Share Your Data

**Communicate** You can visit **physicspp.com/internet_lab** to post the acceleration of your elevator and compare it to other elevators around the country, maybe even the world. Post a description of your elevator's ride so that a comparison of acceleration versus ride comfort can be evaluated.

_____

_____

_____

**Physics** **nline**

To find out more about forces and acceleration, visit the Web site: **physicspp.com**

# CHAPTER
# 4    Study Guide

# Forces in One Dimension
## Vocabulary Review

*Write the term that correctly completes the statement. Use each term once.*

| | | |
|---|---|---|
| agent | force | Newton's second law |
| apparent weight | free-body diagram | Newton's third law |
| contact force | gravitational force | normal force |
| drag force | inertia | system |
| equilibrium | interaction pair | tension |
| external world | net force | terminal velocity |
| field force | Newton's first law | weightlessness |

1. _____ Everything surrounding a system that exerts forces on it is the _____.

2. _____ The attractive force that exists between all objects with mass is the _____.

3. _____ "An object that is at rest will remain at rest, and an object that is moving will continue to move in a straight line with constant speed, if and only if the net force acting on the object is zero." This sentence is a statement of _____.

4. _____ An action exerted on an object that causes a change in motion is a(n) _____.

5. _____ A force that is exerted without contact is a(n) _____.

6. _____ Two forces that are in opposite directions and have equal magnitudes are a(n) _____.

7. _____ A force exerted by any segment of a rope or string on an adjoining segment is _____.

8. _____ The vector sum of two or more forces acting on an object is the _____.

9. _____ The net force on an object in _____ is zero.

10. _____ A force exerted by a fluid on an object moving through the fluid is a(n) _____.

11. _____ "The acceleration of a body is directly proportional to the net force on it and inversely proportional to its mass." This sentence is a statement of _____.

12. _____ The force exerted on a scale by an object and other forces acting upon the object is the _____.

13. _____ A force that acts on an object by touching it is a(n) _____.

14. _____ "The two forces in an interactive pair act on different objects and are equal in magnitude and opposite in direction." This sentence is a statement of _____.

15. _____ A perpendicular contact force exerted by a surface on another object is a(n) _____.

16. _____ A defined object or group of objects is a(n) _____.

17. _____ The tendency of an object to resist changes in its motion is _____.

18. _____ The specific, identifiable cause of a force is the _____.

19. _____ In a(n) _____, a dot represents an object and arrows represent each force acting on it, with their tails on the dot and their points indicating the direction of the force.

20. _____ The constant velocity that a falling object reaches when the drag force equals the force of gravity is its _____.

21. _____ When an object's apparent weight is zero, the object is in a state of _____.

## Section 4.1    Force and Motion

In your textbook, read about Newton's first and second laws and combining forces on pages 92–95.
*For each statement below, write **true** or **false**.*

1. _____ Newton's second law can be written as the equation $a = F_{net}/m$.

2. _____ In the ideal case of zero resistance, a ball rolling on a level surface will accelerate.

3. _____ The acceleration of an object and the net force acting on it are proportional.

4. _____ Force and acceleration are scalar quantities.

5. _____ Gravity is a field force.

6. _____ When the net forces acting on an object sum to zero then the object is accelerating.

7. _____ According to Newton's first law, an object that is moving will continue to move in a straight line and at a constant speed if and only if the net force acting on it is greater than zero.

8. _____ Acceleration is a change in velocity caused by an unbalanced force.

In your textbook, read about free-body diagrams and equilibrium on pages 89 and 95, respectively.
*Refer to the diagrams below to answer questions 9–16. Circle the letter of the choice that best completes
the statement or answers the question.*

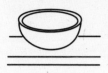

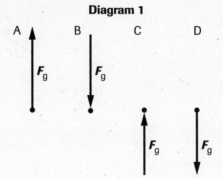

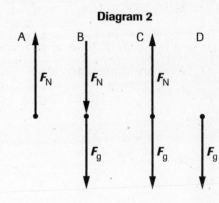

**9.** The agent of $F_N$ is _____.

   **a.** the bowl                **c.** friction

   **b.** Earth                   **d.** the shelf

**10.** The agent of $F_g$ is _____:

   **a.** the bowl                **c.** friction

   **b.** Earth                   **d.** the shelf

**11.** What part of Diagram 2 best represents the bowl in equilibrium?

   **a.** A                    **c.** C

   **b.** B                    **d.** D

**12.** Which part of Diagram 1 best represents the weight force of the bowl sitting on a shelf?

   **a.** A                    **c.** C

   **b.** B                    **d.** D

**13.** $F_N$ is a symbol that represents the _____ force.

   **a.** friction              **c.** normal

   **b.** tension               **d.** weight

**14.** The magnitude of the net force on the bowl in equilibrium is _____.

   **a.** $F_N$                 **c.** 0

   **b.** $F_g$                 **d.** $2F_g$

**15.** Which of these is true when the bowl is in equilibrium?

   **a.** $F_N = F_g$           **c.** $F_N > F_g$

   **b.** $F_N \geq F_g$          **d.** $F_N < F_g$

**16.** Which part of Diagram 2 best represents the bowl if it falls off the shelf?

   **a.** A                                **c.** C

   **b.** B                                **d.** D

*Draw a free-body diagram of each situation.*

**17.** A rocket immediately after
vertical liftoff

**18.** A penny sliding at constant
velocity on a desktop

**19.** A penny immediately after
sliding off a desktop

> **Section 4.2**    **Using Newton's Laws**

In your textbook, read about mass, weight, and apparent weight on pages 96–98.
*For each term on the left, write the letter of the matching item.*

| | | |
|---|---|---|
| _____ | **1.** name of gravitational force acting on object | **a.** $g$ |
| _____ | **2.** magnitude of acceleration due to gravity | **b.** newton |
| _____ | **3.** symbol for the acceleration due to gravity | **c.** weight |
| _____ | **4.** symbol for the force due to gravity | **d.** $9.80 \text{ m/s}^2$ |
| _____ | **5.** expression for the weight of an object | **e.** weightlessness |
| _____ | **6.** unit of force | **f.** $mg$ |
| _____ | **7.** property of an object that does not vary from location to location | **g.** $F_g$ |
| _____ | **8.** having an apparent weight of zero | **h.** mass |

In your textbook, read about scales and apparent weight on pages 96–98.

*Read the description below and refer to the diagram at right to answer questions 9–14. Circle the letter of the choice that best completes the statement or answers the question.*

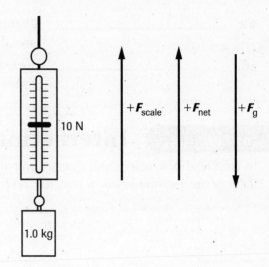

A 1.0-kg mass at rest is suspended from a spring scale. The direction of positive forces that are acting or could act on the 1.0-kg mass are shown to the right.

**9.** The 1.0-kg mass and spring scale are being lifted at a constant speed. The net force on the mass is _____.

   **a.** 0 N                 **c.** −10 N

   **b.** +10 N           **d.** +20 N

**10.** The 1.0-kg mass and spring scale are being lifted so that the 1.0-kg mass is being accelerated in the positive upward direction at 1.0 m/s$^2$. What is the net force acting on the mass?

   **a.** 0 N                 **c.** −1 N

   **b.** +1 N             **d.** +20 N

**11.** In problem 10, what is the relationship among the magnitudes of the forces acting on the mass?

   **a.** $F_{net} = F_{scale} + F_g$         **c.** $F_{net} = -(F_{scale} + F_g)$

   **b.** $F_{net} = F_{scale} - F_g$         **d.** $F_{net} = F_g - F_{scale}$

**12.** In problem 10, what is the spring scale reading?

   **a.** <10 N             **c.** >10 N

   **b.** 10 N               **d.** 0 N

**13.** If the scale is accidentally dropped, the net force acting on the 1.0-kg mass is _____.

   **a.** 0 N                 **c.** −10 N

   **b.** +10 N           **d.** +20 N

**14.** If the scale is accidentally dropped, the reading of the spring scale as it falls is _____.

   **a.** 0 N                 **c.** −10 N

   **b.** +10 N           **d.** +20 N

In your textbook, read about the drag force and terminal velocity on pages 100–101.

*For each statement below, write **true** or rewrite the italicized part to make the statement true.*

**15.** _____ A fluid exerts a drag force on an object moving through it in the *same direction as* the motion of the object.

**16.** _____ The drag force is dependent on the properties of the object, the properties of the fluid the object is moving through, and the *motion of the object.*

**17.** _____ A light object with a large surface area is *less* affected by the drag force than a more compact object is when both objects are falling.

**18.** _____ The terminal velocity of a falling object is reached when *the object impacts on a surface.*

## Section 4.3   Interaction Forces

In your textbook, read about interaction pairs on pages 102–104.

***Refer to the diagram below to complete Table 1.***

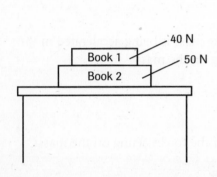

| Table 1 | | |
|---|---|---|
| **Force** | **Magnitude** | **Direction** |
| $F_{\text{book 1 on book 2}}$ | | |
| $F_{\text{book 2 on book 1}}$ | | |
| $F_{\text{book 2 on desktop}}$ | | |
| $F_{\text{desktop on book 2}}$ | | |
| $F_{\text{books 1 and 2 on desktop}}$ | | |
| $F_{\text{desktop on books 1 and 2}}$ | | |

In your textbook, read about tension on pages 105–106.

***For each statement below, write* true *or* false.**

**1.** _____ A book lying on a table involves tension.

**2.** _____ A chandelier hanging from a ceiling involves tension.

**3.** _____ Two teams participating in a tug-of-war involves tension.

**4.** _____ An automobile moving along a road involves tension.

**5.** _____ An elevator moving in a building shaft involves tension.

**6.** _____ A basketball passed from one player to another involves tension.

**7.** _____ A horse pulling a cart involves tension.

**8.** _____ A truck towing a boat behind it involves tension.

**9.** _____ Water skiing involves tension.

**10.** _____ A trapeze act involves tension.

**11.** _____ Paddling a canoe involves tension.

**12.** _____ Parachuting involves tension.

**CHAPTER**
# 4 Section 4-1 Quiz

1. What are the two components that make up a force?

_____

_____

2. How can the forces acting on an object be combined to show the net force acting on an object?

_____

_____

_____

3. What is equilibrium in terms of forces?

_____

_____

_____

4. What is the acceleration of a 35-kg mass that has a force of 270 N applied to it horizontally?

5. A crate is pushed East across a frictionless surface with a force of 240 N and pulled to the East by a rope with a force of 120 N. What is the net force on the crate?

6. What is the mass of an object that can be accelerated horizontally at 4.4 m/s$^2$ by a force of 970 N?

**CHAPTER**
# 4 ~ Section 4-2 Quiz

1. Upon what two factors does the weight of an object depend?

   _____

   _____

   _____

2. Define terminal velocity.

   _____

   _____

   _____

3. Name one situation in which an object is weightless.

   _____

   _____

   _____

4. During a tug-of-war, one side pulls with a force of 12,000.0 N toward the north, and the other side pulls with a force of 12,010.0 toward the south. What is the net force on the mass of all the pullers? You may want to draw a free-body diagram to help you answer the question.

5. While stationary on Earth you have a weight of 550 N. When in an elevator that accelerates upward your weight temporarily becomes 590 N. When descending, your weight temporarily becomes 510 N. You may want to draw a free-body diagram to help you answer these questions.

   a. What is the acceleration you experience as the elevator moves up?

   b. What is the acceleration you experience as the elevator moves down?

*Physics: Principles and Problems*

**CHAPTER**

# 4    Section 4-3 Quiz

1. What are all forces the result of?

_____

_____

_____

2. Define tension.

_____

_____

_____

3. Define normal force.

_____

_____

_____

_____

4. A large safe being lifted into a building with a pulley snaps the chain that supports it and falls toward Earth. If the safe has a mass of 15,000 kg, what is the acceleration of Earth toward the safe?

5. What is the tension in a rope that is being used to accelerate a 200.0-kg crate upward at 1.2 m/s$^2$?

**CHAPTER**

# 4 ~ Reinforcement

## Materials

- large, two-tined cooking fork
- strawberry or slice of fruit
- sink

## Newton's Laws

### Procedure

1. Place a strawberry or a slice of other fruit, such as a peach or melon, on the tines of a large cooking fork. Do the following exercises over the sink.

2. Hold the fork in your right hand, tines pointing upward, and make a fist with your left hand.

3. Hold your left hand steady, and bring your right hand down so that your right wrist strikes your left fist. Note the position of the fruit on the fork.

4. Now hold the fork so that the tines point downward.

5. Repeat the process. **CAUTION:** *Hold the fork so that the tines will not touch your left hand as you bring down your right hand.* Again, note the position of the fruit on the fork.

### Results

1. Describe what happened to the fruit when the tines of the fork pointed upward and your right wrist struck your left fist.

   _____

   _____

   _____

2. How did the motion of the fruit differ from the motion of your hand and the fork? Use Newton's laws to explain how this difference in motion affected the fruit.

   _____

   _____

   _____

   _____

   _____

   _____

   _____

**3.** Describe what happened to the fruit when the tines of the fork pointed downward and your right wrist struck your left fist.

_____

_____

_____

**4.** Use Newton's laws to explain the motion of the fruit. Explain why the final position of the fruit differs when the tines of the fork point upward from when they point downward.

_____

_____

_____

_____

_____

**CHAPTER**

# 4 ⎯ Enrichment

## Materials

- large plastic basin with a smooth bottom
- water
- thin strong string such as dental floss
- variety of small objects more dense than water
- small spring scale
- stopwatch
- metric ruler

## Factors Affecting Drag

When an object moves through a fluid such as water or air, the fluid exerts a force called a drag force that opposes the motion of the object. In this activity, you will design experiments to test the effect of various factors on drag force.

### Procedure

You will design and conduct two experiments. For both experiments, write a hypothesis and perform repeated trials. Be sure to control variables—in other words, make sure to change only one factor at a time in your experiment. Work in groups of two.

**CAUTION:** *Have your experiments approved by your teacher before carrying them out.*

First, design an experiment to test the effect of the speed of an object on the drag force.

1. What is your hypothesis for your first experiment?

   _____

   _____

   _____

   _____

2. How will you test your hypothesis in your first experiment?

   _____

   _____

   _____

   _____

Next, design an experiment to test the effect of the shape of an object on the drag force.

3. What is your hypothesis for your second experiment?

   _____

   _____

   _____

   _____

**4.** How will you test your hypothesis in your second experiment?

_____

_____

_____

_____

_____

## Results

**1.** What did you conclude from your first experiment? Was your hypothesis supported?

_____

_____

_____

_____

**2.** What did you conclude from your second experiment? Was your hypothesis supported?

_____

_____

_____

_____

**3.** What are some possible sources of error in your experiments?

_____

_____

_____

**4.** How could you test the effects of temperature on the drag force? *CAUTION: Do not do this experiment unless it is approved by your teacher.*

_____

_____

_____

**5.** Why do you think that drag force is affected by temperature?

_____

_____

_____

# Combining Forces on an Object

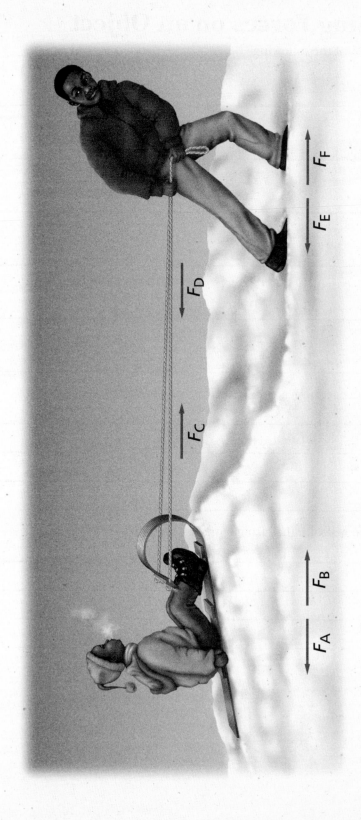

# 4 ⬟ Transparency 4-1 Worksheet

# Combining Forces on an Object

**1.** Define each of the following:

   **a.** $F_A$

_____

   **b.** $F_B$

_____

   **c.** $F_C$

_____

   **d.** $F_D$

_____

   **e.** $F_E$

_____

   **f.** $F_F$

_____

**2.** List all of the action-reaction pairs.

_____

_____

_____

_____

**3.** What is the net force that actually moves the sled?

_____

_____

_____

_____

# Motion and Newton's Second Law

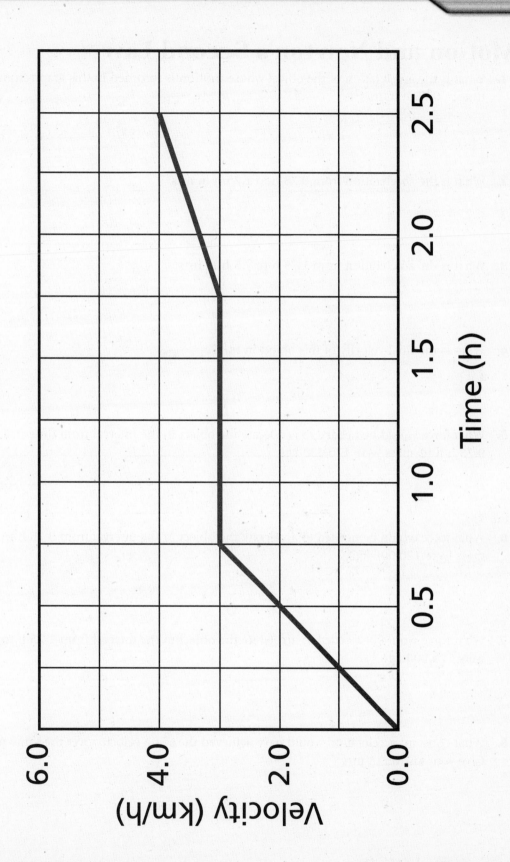

# 4 ⌐‾‾‾⟍ Transparency 4-2 Worksheet

# Motion and Newton's Second Law

1. What is the acceleration of the object whose motion is recorded in this graph from time = 0.0 to time = 0.75 h in m/s$^2$?

2. What is the acceleration from 0.75 h to 1.75 h in m/s$^2$?

3. What is the acceleration from 1.75 h to 2.5 h in m/s$^2$?

4. What is the final velocity of this object in m/s?

5. What force would be needed to accelerate the object in the interval from time = 0.0 h to time = 0.75 h if its mass were 120,000 kg?

6. What force would be needed to accelerate the object in the interval from 0.75 h to 1.75 h if its mass were 120,000 kg?

7. What force would be needed to accelerate the object in the interval from 1.75 h to 2.5 h if its mass were 120,000 kg?

8. What constant acceleration would have achieved the same velocity over the same period of time? Give your answer in m/s$^2$.

# Newton's Third Law: Interaction Pairs

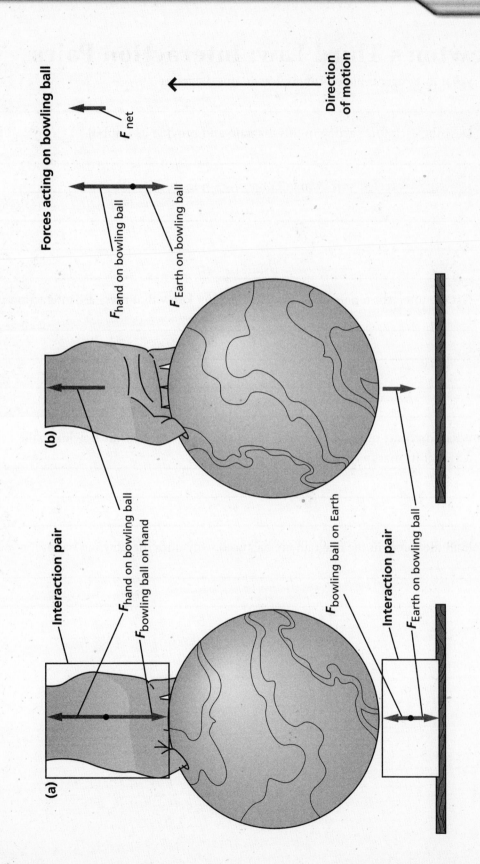

# 4 ▃▃ **Transparency 4-3 Worksheet**

# Newton's Third Law: Interaction Pairs

**1.** What three agents are exerting forces in this diagram?

_____

**2.** Describe each force acting in this diagram and provide its symbol.

_____

_____

_____

_____

_____

**3.** List the interaction pairs of forces. How do you know that these are interaction pairs?

_____

_____

_____

_____

**4.** What forces act only on the hand? Only on Earth? Only on the bowling ball?

_____

_____

_____

**5.** If all the forces in the diagram are balanced, why does the bowling ball not remain stationary?

_____

_____

# Weight and Normal Force

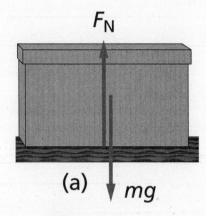

(a) $F_N$ ... $mg$

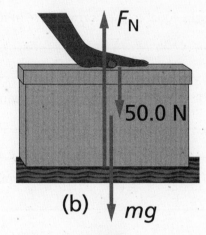

(b) $F_N$ ... 50.0 N ... $mg$

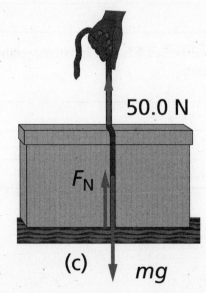

(c) 50.0 N ... $F_N$ ... $mg$

# 4 Transparency 4-4 Worksheet

# Weight and Normal Force

**1.** Define *weight*.

_____

_____

_____

**2.** Define *normal force*.

_____

_____

_____

_____

**3.** In which figure is the box's weight equal to the normal force in magnitude?

_____

_____

**4.** In which figure is the magnitude of the normal force greater than the weight of the box?

_____

_____

**5.** Are mass and gravity the only factors that contribute to the normal force of an object?

_____

_____

_____

**6.** In which figure (or figures) does the box have an apparent weight different from that caused by its mass and the effect of gravity alone?

_____

_____

_____

_____

**CHAPTER**

# 4 — Chapter Assessment

# Forces

## Understanding Physics Concepts

*Circle the letter of the choice that best completes the statement.*

1. Moving faster as you pedal your bicycle harder on a level road demonstrates Newton's _____ law.

   **a.** first                    **c.** third

   **b.** second                   **d.** gravity

2. According to Newton's _____ law, an object with no net force acting on it remains at rest or in motion with a constant velocity.

   **a.** first                    **c.** third

   **b.** second                   **d.** apple

3. If you push against a wall, the wall pushes back against you with _____ force.

   **a.** no                       **c.** equal

   **b.** less                     **d.** more

4. An object is in equilibrium if _____.

   **a.** it has no weight         **c.** it is accelerating

   **b.** the net force on it is zero   **d.** only one force is acting on it

5. Mass and weight are related by _____.

   **a.** the force of gravity     **c.** friction

   **b.** newtons                  **d.** inertia

6. The gravitational force exerted by a large body, such as Earth, is _____.

   **a.** weight                   **c.** acceleration

   **b.** mass                     **d.** apparent weight

7. The force exerted by any segment of a string or rope on an adjoining segment is _____.

   **a.** the drag force           **c.** friction

   **b.** tension                  **d.** the force of gravity

8. The normal force is the _____ force exerted by a surface on another object.

   **a.** perpendicular field      **c.** perpendicular contact

   **b.** parallel contact         **d.** parallel field

9. The force exerted by a fluid on an object moving through the fluid is _____.

   **a.** tension                  **c.** the drag force

   **b.** thrust                   **d.** the force of gravity

**10.** When the drag force on an object equals the force of gravity, the object attains _____ .

    **a.** acceleration                   **c.** terminal velocity

    **b.** apparent weight             **d.** maximum mass

*Complete the statement by writing the correct term in the space provided.*

**11.** _____ An object that experiences a push or a pull has a _____ exerted on it.

**12.** _____ Forces have both direction and _____ .

**13.** _____ In a free-body diagram, you draw the force vectors leading _____ the object.

**14.** _____ You can add the forces acting upon an object by using _____ addition to find the net force.

**15.** _____ An object with no net force acting on it is in _____ .

**16.** _____ The weight of an object depends upon the acceleration due to _____ and the mass of the object.

**17.** _____ An object with no apparent weight experiences _____ .

**18.** _____ The effect of drag on an object's motion is determined by the object's _____ and its _____ .

**19.** _____ All forces result from _____ between objects.

**20.** _____ According to Newton's third law, the two forces that make up an interaction pair are equal in _____ , but _____ in direction.

**21.** _____ Tension is the specific name for the force exerted by a(n) _____ .

**22.** _____ The _____ force is a support force resulting from the contact of two objects.

## Thinking Critically

*Answer the following questions. Use complete sentences.*

1. Explain the relationship between mass and weight on Earth. Would this relationship change on the planet Mars? Give a reason for your answer.

   _____

   _____

   _____

   _____

   _____

2. You are in an elevator traveling from the lobby to the top of a building. As it slows to a stop on the top floor, what happens to your apparent weight?

   _____

   _____

   _____

   _____

3. In the drawing below, use arrows to show the two horizontal and two vertical forces acting on the boat as it is pulled to the shore at a constant speed. Is there a net force on the boat? Explain.

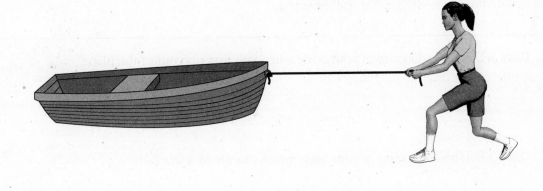

   _____

   _____

   _____

**4.** Explain what is meant by an interaction pair. Use the boat in the drawing for question 3 to give an example.

_____

_____

_____

_____

_____

_____

**5.** Suppose you pull on a rope tied to a large carton, but you cannot move the carton. What forces are acting on your hand? Draw a free-body diagram.

_____

_____

_____

**6.** You are skydiving. The plane takes you to a typical jump altitude of 3000 m. When you step out of the plane, you accelerate downward at 190 kph for about 10 s. Then you enter 45 s of free fall—this is when you fall at terminal velocity. At 760 m your parachute deploys. If you want to experience more time in free fall, what should you do?

_____

**a.** Draw a free-body diagram of your body when you first step out of the plane.

**b.** Draw a free-body diagram of your body when you are in a free fall.

**c.** Draw a free-body diagram of your body immediately after your parachute has deployed.

## Applying Physics Knowledge

*Answer the following questions. Show your calculations.*

**1.** What force is required to accelerate a 6.0-kg bowling ball at $+2.0 \text{ m/s}^2$?

**2.** What is the mass of a cat that weighs 30.0 N?

**3.** What is the tension in a rope that is supporting a 4.2-kg bucket?

**4.** A net force of $+125$ N acts on an object. Find the single force that will produce equilibrium.

*Answer the following questions. Show your calculations. Draw a free-body diagram to help you answer the questions.*

**5.** An elevator with a mass of $1.10 \times 10^3$ kg accelerates upward at $0.45 \text{ m/s}^2$. What is the force acting on the elevator's support cable?

**6.** A rocket weighs $2.0 \times 10^7$ N. Its engines exert a force of $+25 \times 10^6$ N at liftoff.

**a.** What is the mass of the rocket at liftoff?

**b.** What is the rocket's acceleration when it lifts off?

**7.** A 47-N box is pulled along a frictionless horizontal surface by a 25-N weight hanging from a cord on a frictionless pulley.

**a.** What is the acceleration of the box and the weight?

**b.** What force is exerted on the cord?

**8.** A stepping stool is constructed so that it collapses when the normal force exceeds 1100 N. You are assisting a welder who weighs 102 kg and is on the top step of the stepping stool. You pass the welder a torch and a fuel tank that weigh a combined 14 kg. The welder refuses to take both items from you. Explain why. Show your calculations.

## Forces in Two Dimensions

**CHAPTER**
# 5 ___ Mini Lab Worksheet

## What's Your Angle?  🥽 🖐️

Prop a board up so that it forms an inclined plane at a 45° angle. Hang a 500-g object from the spring scale.

1. **Measure** and record the weight of the object. Set the object on the bottom of the board and slowly pull it up the inclined plane at a constant speed.

2. **Observe and record** the reading on the spring scale.

| Weight of the Object | Spring Scale Reading | Component of Weight |
|---|---|---|
|  |  |  |
|  |  |  |
|  |  |  |
|  |  |  |
|  |  |  |

## Analyze and Conclude

3. **Calculate** the component of weight for the 500-g object that is parallel to the inclined plane.


4. **Compare** the spring-scale reading along the inclined plane with the component of weight parallel to the inclined plane.

_____

_____

_____

**CHAPTER**

# 5 Physics Lab Worksheet

## Materials

- pulley
- C-clamp
- masking tape
- wood surface
- string (1 m)
- spring scale, 0–5 N
- wood block

# The Coefficient of Friction

Static and kinetic friction are forces that are a result of two surfaces in contact with each other. Static friction is the force that must be overcome to cause an object to begin moving, while kinetic friction occurs between two objects in motion relative to each other. The kinetic friction force, $F_{f, \text{kinetic}}$, is defined by $F_{f, \text{kinetic}} = \mu_k F_N$, where $\mu_k$ is the coefficient of kinetic friction and $F_N$ is the normal force acting on the object. The maximum static frictional force, $F_{f, \text{max static}}$, is defined by $F_{f, \text{static}} = \mu_s F_N$ where $\mu_s$ is the coefficient of static friction and $F_N$ is the normal force on the object. The maximum static frictional force that must be overcome before movement is able to begin is $\mu_s F_N$. If you apply a constant force to pull an object along a horizontal surface at a constant speed, then the frictional force opposing the motion is equal and opposite to the applied force, $F_p$. Therefore, $F_p = F_f$. The normal force is equal and opposite to the object's weight when the object is on a horizontal surface and the applied force is horizontal.

## Question

How can the coefficient of static and kinetic friction be determined for an object on a horizontal surface?

## Objectives

- **Measure** the normal and frictional forces acting on an object starting in motion and already in motion.
- **Use numbers** to calculate $\mu_s$ and $\mu_k$.
- **Compare and contrast** values of $\mu_s$ and $\mu_k$.
- **Analyze** the kinetic friction results.
- **Estimate** the angle where sliding will begin for an object on an inclined plane.

## Procedure

1. Check your spring scale to make sure that it reads zero when held vertically. If necessary, follow your teacher's instructions to zero it.
2. Attach the pulley to the edge of the table with a C-clamp.
3. Attach the string to the spring scale hook and the wood block.
4. Measure the weight of the block of wood or other small object and record the value as the normal force, $F_N$, in Data Tables 1, 2, and 3.
5. Unhook the string from the spring scale and run it through the pulley. Then reattach it to the spring scale.
6. Move the wood block as far away from the pulley as the string permits while still keeping it on the wood surface.

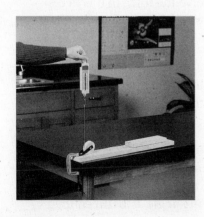

# 5  Physics Lab Worksheet

| Material Table | |
|---|---|
| **Object material** | |
| **Surface material** | |

| Data Table 1 | | | | |
|---|---|---|---|---|
| $F_N$(N) | **Static Friction Force, $F_s$(N)** | | | |
| | **Trial 1** | **Trial 2** | **Trial 3** | **Average** |
| | | | | |
| | | | | |

| Data Table 3 | | | | |
|---|---|---|---|---|
| $F_N$(N) | $F_s$(N) | $F_f$(N) | $\mu_s$ | $\mu_k$ |
| | | | | |
| | | | | |

| Data Table 2 | | | | |
|---|---|---|---|---|
| $F_N$(N) | **Kinetic Friction Force, $F_f$(N)** | | | |
| | **Trial 1** | **Trial 2** | **Trial 3** | **Average** |
| | | | | |
| | | | | |

| Data Table 4  (Angle, $\theta$, when sliding begins on an incline) | |
|---|---|
| $\theta^*$ | **tan $\theta^*$** |
| | |
| | |

7. With the spring scale oriented vertically so that a right angle is formed between the wood block, the pulley, and the spring scale, slowly pull up on the spring scale. Observe the force that is necessary to cause the wood block to begin sliding. Record this value for the static friction force in Data Table 1.

8. Repeat steps 6 and 7 for two additional trials.

9. Repeat steps 6 and 7. However, once the block begins sliding, pull just hard enough to keep it moving at a constant speed across the other horizontal surface. Record this force as the kinetic friction force in Data Table 2.

10. Repeat step 9 for two additional trials.

11. Place the block on the end of the surface. Slowly raise one end of the surface to make an incline. Gently tap the block to cause it to move and overcome static friction. If the block stops, replace it at the top of the incline and repeat the procedure. Continue increasing the angle, $\theta$, between the horizontal and the inclined surface and tapping the block until it slides at a constant speed down the incline. Record the angle, $\theta$, in Data Table 4.

## Analyze

**1.** Average the data for the static friction force, $F_{s, max}$, from the three trials and record the result in the last column of Data Table 1 and in Data Table 3.

**2.** Average the data for the kinetic friction force, $F_f$, from the three trials and record the result in the last column of Data Table 2 and in Data Table 3.

**3.** Use the data in Data Table 3 to calculate the coefficient of static friction, $\mu_s$, and record the value in Data Table 3.

**4.** Use the data in Data Table 3 to calculate the coefficient of kinetic friction, $\mu_k$, and record the value in Data Table 3.

**5.** Calculate $\tan \theta$ for your value in Data Table 4.

## Conclude and Apply

**1.** **Compare and Contrast** Examine your values for $\mu_s$ and $\mu_k$. Explain whether your results are reasonable or not.

_____

_____

_____

_____

**2.** **Use Models** Draw a free-body diagram showing the forces acting on the block if it is placed on an incline of angle $\theta$. Make certain that you include the force due to friction in your diagram.

**3.** From your diagram, assuming that the angle, $\theta$, is where sliding begins, what does tan $\theta$ represent?

_____

_____

_____

_____

**4.** Compare your value for tan $\theta$ (experimental), $\mu_s$, and $\mu_k$.

_____

_____

_____

_____

## Going Further

Repeat the experiment with additional surfaces that have different characteristics.

_____

_____

_____

_____

## Real-World Physics

If you were downhill skiing and wished to determine the coefficient of kinetic friction between your skis and the slope, how could you do this? Be specific about how you could find a solution to this problem.

_____

_____

_____

_____

_____

_____

_____

**Physics** *nline*

To find out more about friction, visit the Web site:
**physicspp.com**

## CHAPTER
# 5    Study Guide

# Forces in Two Dimensions
## Vocabulary Review
*Write the term that correctly completes the statement. Use each term once.*

| | | |
|---|---|---|
| coefficient of kinetic friction | equilibrant | static friction |
| coefficient of static friction | kinetic friction | vector resolution |
| component | | |

**1.** _____ To determine the _____ of a vector, a coordinate system must be chosen.

**2.** _____ The force of _____ depends on the normal force exerted by an object when there is no motion between the two surfaces.

**3.** _____ The _____ is a force that puts an object into equilibrium.

**4.** _____ _____ is always less than the maximum value of static friction.

**5.** _____ The _____ is needed to calculate the force of kinetic friction.

**6.** _____ Breaking a vector down into its components is called _____.

**7.** _____ The _____ is greater than the coefficient of kinetic friction.

## Section 5.1   Vectors

In your textbook, read about vectors on pages 119–125.
*For each statement below, write* **true** *or rewrite the italicized part to make it true.*

**1.** _____ The representation of a vector has both *length* and direction.

**2.** _____ Velocity and speed are both quantities, but only *speed* is a vector.

**3.** _____ *Mass* is not a vector.

**4.** _____ *Force* is a vector because it has both length and direction.

**5.** _____ When you represent a vector on a coordinate system, the tail of the vector *is always* placed on the origin.

**6.** _____ If two vectors are represented on a coordinate system, and they point in the same direction and have the same length, the vectors are *equivalent*.

**7.** _____ When adding two vectors on a graph, you place them *tail*-to-tail.

*For the following combinations of vectors, draw the resultant vector by connecting the tip of one vector to the tail of the other.*

**8.**  ——————————→    —————————————→

**9.**  ◄——————————    ◄——————————

**10.**

**11.**

*Circle the letter of the choice that best completes the statement.*

**12.** When adding two vectors that are perpendicular, it is best to use _____.

    **a.** the Pythagorean theorem        **c.** the law of sines

    **b.** the law of cosines               **d.** a free-body diagram

**13.** The law of sines is _____.

    **a.** $R^2 = A^2 + B^2$               **c.** $R^2 = A^2 + B^2 - 2AB \cos \theta$

    **b.** $\dfrac{R}{\sin \theta} = \dfrac{A}{\sin a} = \dfrac{B}{\sin b}$       **d.** $A = A_x + A_y$

**14.** If you know three sides of a triangle but do not know any of the angles, you must use the _____ to find one of the angles.

    **a.** Pythagorean theorem        **c.** law of sines

    **b.** law of cosines                **d.** resultant vector

*Using graph paper, protractor, and ruler, solve the following problems using graphical methods. Check your answer by calculating the resultant vector's direction and length using trigonometry. Show your calculations.*

**15.** A man walks 5.0 m east and then 10 m north. What is the direction and length of his total displacement?

**16.** An airplane is traveling 600.0 m/s at 35° degrees north of east when a tail wind starts to blow. The velocity of the tail wind is 100.0 m/s 15° west of north. What are the new direction and speed of the airplane?

In your textbook read about vectors on pages 119–125.
*Answer the following questions. Use complete sentences and show your calculations.*

**17.** Why is vector resolution the opposite of vector addition?

_____

_____

**18.** Three small children are pulling a rag doll in different directions, each trying to get the doll from the other two. The x-component of the force exerted by the first child is 5.0 N, and the y-component is 3.0 N. The second child's force is −4.0 N in the x-direction and 2.0 N in the y-direction. The x- and y- directions of the third force are 1.0 N and −8.0 N. What are the components of the net force acting on the rag doll? What is the direction and magnitude of the net force? You may want to draw a free-body diagram to help you solve the problem.

*The following steps for adding vectors are in scrambled order. In the space provided, write which step is first, second, third, and fourth.*

_____ **19.** Move vectors so they are tip-to-tail.

_____ **20.** Measure the length and direction of resultant vector.

_____ **21.** Choose a scale and draw the vectors.

_____ **22.** Draw the resultant vector.

## Section 5.2 ⬤ **Friction**

In your textbook, read about friction on pages 126–130.

*Circle the letter of the choice that best completes the statement or answers the question.*

1. A box with a mass of 10 kg is at rest on a table. The normal force acting on the box is _____.

   **a.** 10 kg upward                    **c.** 98 N upward

   **b.** 9.8 N upward                    **d.** 989 downward

2. An ice-skater who weighs 200 N is gliding across the ice. If the force of friction is 4 N, what is the coefficient of kinetic friction?

   **a.** 50          **b.** 0.02          **c.** 4          **d.** 4 N

3. A sofa is at rest on the floor. The mass of the sofa is 150 kg and the coefficient of static friction between the sofa and the floor is 0.30. The maximum force of static friction is approximately _____.

   **a.** 150 N        **b.** 1500 N        **c.** 440 N        **d.** 4500 N

4. A team of dogs is pulling a heavy sled through the snow in the direction of east. The direction of the force of friction is _____.

   **a.** east          **b.** upward          **c.** west          **d.** downward

5. A mover of household goods wants to push a heavy bureau at rest on the floor across the floor. He puts his shoulder against the bureau and begins to push. He gradually increases the force of his push until the bureau moves when he keeps the pushing force constant. The force of friction _____.

   **a.** decreases and then increases          **c.** remains the same

   **b.** increases and then decreases          **d.** continues to increase

*Refer to the passage below to answer questions 6–8.*

A crate with a mass of 1000 kg is being pulled along greased tracks by a winch. The winch is exerting a force of 2000 N in the horizontal direction along the tracks. The coefficient of kinetic friction between the crate and the tracks is 0.2.

6. Draw a free-body diagram of the crate showing the force of gravity, the pulling force, and the force of friction.

**7.** What is the net force acting on the crate in the horizontal direction?

**8.** Using Newton's second law, calculate the acceleration of the crate.

**Section 5.3** **Force and Motion in Two Dimensions**

In your textbook, read about force and motion in two dimensions on pages 131–135.

*Circle the letter of the choice that best completes the statement or answers the question.*

**1.** The equilibrant of a force directed 45° west of north has the direction _____.

    **a.** 45° west of north         **c.** 45° south of east

    **b.** 45° east of north         **d.** 45° west of south

**2.** The equilibrant of force in the positive $x$-direction and a force in the positive $y$-direction is directed from the origin to the _____.

    **a.** first quadrant         **c.** third quadrant

    **b.** second quadrant         **d.** fourth quadrant

**3.** The magnitude of the equilibrant of a 3 N force acting toward the east and a 4 N force acting toward the south is _____.

    **a.** 7 N         **b.** 5 N         **c.** 1 N         **d.** −7 N

*Refer to the passage below to answer questions 4–9.*

A toy sled with a mass of 1.0 kg is sliding down a ramp that makes an angle of 25° with the ground. The coefficient of kinetic friction between the toy sled and the ramp is 0.25.

**4.** In a coordinate system where the $x$-axis is parallel to the ramp and the $y$-axis is perpendicular to the ramp, what are the components of the toy sled's weight?

**5.** In a coordinate system where the $x$-axis is parallel to the ground and the $y$-axis is perpendicular to the ground, what are the component's of the toy sled's weight?

**6.** What is the normal force acting on the toy sled?

**7.** What is the magnitude and direction of the force of friction acting on the toy sled?

**8.** In a coordinate system where the $x$-axis is parallel to the ramp and the $y$-axis is perpendicular to the ramp, what is the net force acting on the toy sled along the $x$-axis?

**9.** Using Newton's second law, calculate the acceleration of the toy sled as it moves down the ramp.

*Refer to the passage below to answer questions 10–12.*

> Workers on the back of a truck gently place a crate with a mass of 200.0 kg on a ramp going down to the ground. The angle the ramp makes with the ground is 30°. The crate does not slide down the ramp but is held in place by the force of static friction.

**10.** Draw a free-body diagram showing all of the forces acting on the crate.

**11.** Draw a second diagram showing the components of all the forces acting on the grate in a coordinate system that makes it easy to apply the law of friction.

**12.** Calculate the coefficient of static friction between the ramp and the crate by assuming that the coefficient is the minimum coefficient needed to keep the crate from sliding.

**CHAPTER**
# 5 ___ Section 5-1 Quiz

1. A salesperson leaves the office and drives 26 km due north along a straight highway. A turn is made onto a highway that leads in the direction 30.0° north of east. The driver continues on the highway for a distance of 62 km and then stops. Using graphical methods, what is the total displacement of the salesperson from the office?

2. A teacher is giving a lesson on vectors. He takes four paces across the classroom, does an about turn, and takes two paces back. He says to the class, "What is the total?" One student says, "two paces." Another student says, "six paces." What would you say if you were in the class? Explain your answer.

_____

_____

3. A heavy box is pulled across a wooden floor with a rope. The rope forms an angle of 60.0° with the floor. A tension of 80.0° N is maintained on the rope. What are the horizontal and vertical components of the force?

4. A hiker leaves camp and walks 10.0 km due north. The hiker then walks 20.0 km in the direction 45° west of north. Using the law of cosines, what is the total distance the hiker walks?

**CHAPTER**

# 5 — Section 5-2 Quiz

1. A 525-N trunk is place on an inclined plane that forms an angle of 30.0° with the horizontal. What are the components of the weight parallel to the plane and normal to the plane?

2. A box rests on a plank that is inclined to the horizontal. As the angle between the plank and the horizontal increases, does the component of the weight of the box parallel to the plank increase, decrease, or remain the same? Explain your answer.

_____

_____

_____

_____

3. An automobile weighing 12,000 N is parked on a 36° slope. Draw the free-body diagram showing all of the forces acting on the automobile.

4. A 32-N force acts on a small mass in the positive $x$-direction. A 26-N force also acts on it in the negative $x$-direction. What is the equilibrant of these two forces? You may want to draw a free-body diagram to help you solve the problem.

5. A child with a mass of 30.0 kg is moving down a slide at a playground. The angle the slide makes with the ground is 60.0°, and the coefficient of friction between the child and the slide is 0.250. What is the frictional force on the child? You may want to draw a free-body diagram to help you solve the problem.

*Physics: Principles and Problems*

**CHAPTER**
# 5 ⎯⎯ Section 5-3 Quiz

1. A man is trying to push a 200.0-kg chest of drawers at rest on the floor. The coefficient of static friction between the floor and the chest of drawers is 0.45. How much horizontal force must he exert on the chest of drawers to move it? You may want to draw a free-body diagram to help you solve the problem.

2. An empty wooden crate is slid across a warehouse floor. If the crate was filled, would the coefficient of kinetic friction between the crate and the floor increase, decrease, or remain the same? Explain your answer.

_____

_____

3. A team of dogs is pulling a sled that has a load of 2500 kg at a constant speed of 5.0 m/s. The coefficient of kinetic friction between the sled and the snow is 0.10. What is the horizontal force the dogs are exerting on the loaded sled? You may want to draw a free-body diagram to help you solve the problem.

4. A wooden block is at rest on a wooden inclined plane that makes a small angle with the horizontal. As the angle increases, does the force of static friction between the block and the plane decrease, increase, or remain the same?

_____

_____

5. An object initially at rest on a horizontal surface is set into motion by the application of a force. Does the force of friction between the object and the surface decrease, increase, or remain the same immediately after the object starts to move?

_____

_____

6. Suppose that your car is stuck on ice. The wheels spin, but the car does not move. Your friend suggests that you let the air out of the tires to increase the amount of friction. What are some reasons your friend might think this? Discuss whether or not these reasons are consistent with what you have learned about friction.

_____

_____

# CHAPTER
# 5 ~~~ Reinforcement

### Materials

- protractor
- ruler

## Forces in Two Dimensions

### Problem

How do you add vectors using graphical methods?

### Procedure

1. On the graph below, draw a coordinate system with the horizontal axis representing the east and west direction and the vertical axis representing the north and south direction.

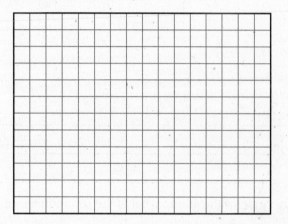

2. Represent the velocity of an airplane going 60 m/s in the direction 30° north of east by drawing an arrow with the tail at the origin and the tip pointing in this direction. Decide on a scale (for example, 1 cm = 10 m/s) and use the protractor to measure the angle and the ruler to measure the length of the line.

3. Represent the velocity of wind that begins to blow on the airplane with a speed of 8 m/s going in the direction 75° south of west in the same way.

4. Add the velocity of the wind to the velocity of the plane by drawing the wind vector a second time with the tail of the wind vector touching the tip of the airplane vector.

**5.** Draw the resultant velocity by drawing a new vector with the tail at the origin and the tip touching the head of the second wind vector.

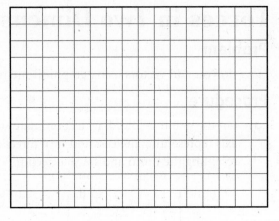

## Results

**1.** How many centimeters long is the resultant vector?

_____

_____

_____

**2.** Using the scale of the graph, what is the resultant speed of the airplane after the wind starts blowing?

_____

_____

_____

**3.** Using the protractor, what is the angle the resultant vector makes with the horizontal axis?

_____

_____

_____

**4.** Using compass directions, what is the direction of the airplane's resultant velocity?

_____

_____

_____

**CHAPTER**

# 5 Enrichment

**Materials**

- graph paper
- protractor
- ruler

# Forces in Two Dimensions

## Problem

How much tension must a 20.0-m-long wire be able to exert without breaking when it is used to hang an iron sculpture that weighs $5.0 \times 10^3$ N? The wire must be attached to two anchors in the ceiling 15.0 m apart.

## Procedure

1. On a piece of graph paper draw an isosceles obtuse triangle representing the hanging sculpture. Decide on a convenient scale (for example 1 cm = 1 m) so that two sides are 10.0 m long and the third side 15.0 m long.

2. Using a protractor, measure the three angles in the triangle.

3. Letting $T$ be the unknown tension in both of the wires and using the angles determined above, draw a vector diagram showing all of the forces acting on the sculpture.

4. Draw another vector diagram showing the horizontal and vertical components of the tension in the wire.

5. Look up the sine and cosine of the angles made by the wires and correctly label the vector diagram in the previous drawing.

6. Use the equilibrium condition in the vertical direction to write down an equation for the tension $T$.

7. Solve the equation for the tension $T$.

## Results

1. What are the three angles of the triangle as measured with a protractor?

_____

_____

2. What are the three angles of the triangle as calculated by using the law of cosines ?

_____

_____

3. Using the tables of trigonometry, what are the horizontal and vertical components of the tension in the wire?

_____

_____

**4.** What is the equilibrium equation in the vertical direction?

_____

_____

**5.** What tension must the wires be able to withstand?

_____

_____

**6.** What tension would the wires have to withstand if the two ends of the wire were attached to a single anchor?

_____

_____

_____

**7.** Why would the museum curator want to have the sculpture suspended from two anchors instead of one?

_____

_____

_____

**8.** Suppose the artist insisted that the work not be suspended symmetrically, but that the distance from one anchor to the sculpture one be 9 m and the distance to the other anchor be 11 meters. Would this be possible to do? Explain your answer.

_____

_____

_____

**9.** If the sculpture was not hung symmetrically, would the tension in the wire be the same on both sides? Explain your answer.

_____

_____

_____

**10.** If the sculpture was not hung symmetrically, could you still calculate the maximum strength needed in the cable? Explain your answer.

_____

_____

_____

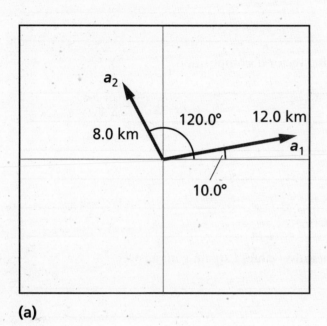

(a)

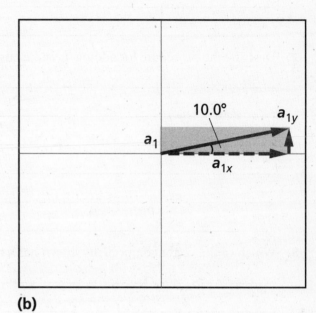

(b)

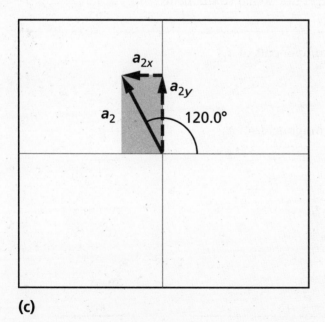

(c)

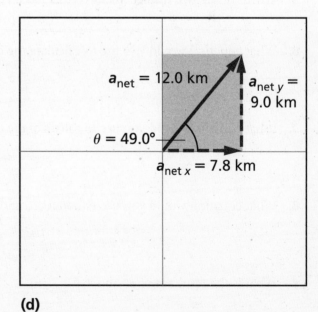

(d)

# 5 ~ Transparency 5-1 Worksheet

# Vector Components

**1.** Are vectors $a_1$ and $a_2$ perpendicular? If not, what is the angle between them?

_____

_____

**2.** Describe the procedure for adding $a_1$ and $a_2$ using vector decomposition.

_____

_____

_____

_____

_____

**3.** Which of the vector components shown has a negative value? Explain your answer.

_____

_____

**4.** Which of the two displacement vectors has a larger vertical component?

_____

**5.** Which of the two displacement vectors has a larger horizontal component?

_____

**6.** What equation would you use to calculate the components of $a_1$?

**7.** What equation would you use to calculate the components of $a_2$?

**8.** What equation would you use to add $a_{net\ x}$ and $a_{net\ y}$?

**9.** What is the resultant of $a_1$ and $a_2$?

# Surfaces and Friction

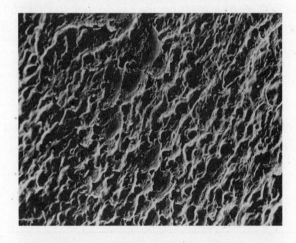

# 5 ___ Transparency 5-2 Worksheet

# Surfaces and Friction

1. Suppose an etched glass plate with a mass of 2 kg is stacked on top of another etched glass plate. The coefficient of static friction between the plates is 0.50. The coefficient of kinetic friction between the plates is 0.20. You want to slide the plates off each other. What is the minimum force you need to apply to the top plate to get it to move?

2. Once the plate is sliding, what minimum force is needed to keep it sliding?

3. Suppose you are sanding an etched glass plate with a piece of sandpaper. The coefficient of static friction between the plate and the sandpaper is 0.90. The coefficient of kinetic friction between the plate and the sandpaper is 0.75. You push on the sandpaper so that you are applying a vertical force of 40 N and a horizontal force of 40 N. Will the sandpaper slide across the plate? Why or why not?

   _____

4. Looking at the photos of the etched glass plate and the sandpaper, what do you think causes the high coefficients of friction between these surfaces?

   _____

   _____

   _____

5. The coefficient of kinetic friction between two sheets of paper is 0.29. Looking at the photo of paper, what do you think is the reason for the relatively low coefficent of kinetic friction?

   _____

   _____

   _____

6. Based on the photo of sandpaper, do you think the coefficients of static and kinetic friction of two pieces of sandpaper rubbing against each other would be relatively high or low? Explain your answer.

   _____

   _____

   _____

# Static Friction

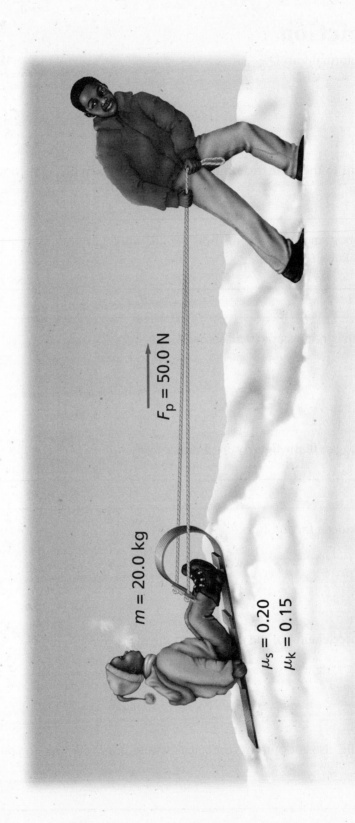

$F_p = 50.0$ N

$m = 20.0$ kg

$\mu_s = 0.20$
$\mu_k = 0.15$

# 5    Transparency 5-3 Worksheet

## Static Friction

1. What is the normal force?

2. What happens to the static friction force as a force is gradually applied to the rope on the front of the toboggan?

   _____

3. When the toboggan is not moving, how are the pulling force and the static friction force related? How do you know?

   _____

   _____

4. What is the maximum static friction force?

5. Will the toboggan in the figure move? Why or why not?

   _____

   _____

6. What is the kinetic friction force?

7. What is the acceleration of the toboggan in the figure?

8. If a 15-kg child also got onto the toboggan, would it move? How do you know?

   _____

   _____

# Forces on an Inclined Plane

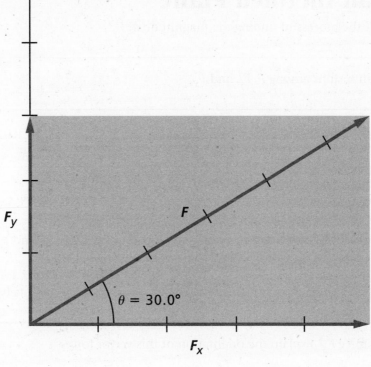

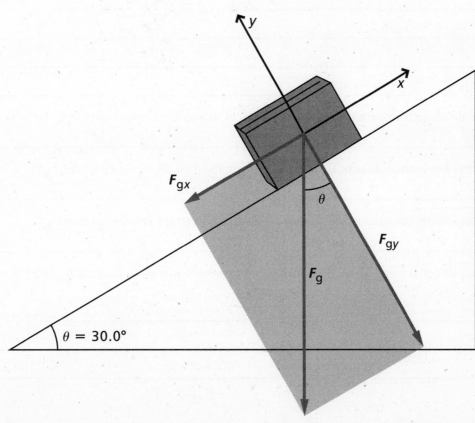

## 5    Transparency 5-4 Worksheet

# Forces on an Inclined Plane

**1.** What do you call the process of finding the magnitude of $F_y$?

_____

**2.** Describe the relationships among $F$, $F_y$, and $F_x$.

_____

_____

_____

**3.** If $F_x$ were negative, how would the diagram be different?

_____

**4.** If you only knew the values of $F$ and $F_x$, what equation could you use to find $F_y$?

_____

**5.** If you increased the angle at which $F$ acts to 40.0°, how will the components be affected?

_____

**6.** What causes the force $F_g$? Explain the orientation of this vector force.

_____

_____

_____

_____

**7.** If the angle of decline were decreased to 15°, how would the components of $F_g$ be affected?

_____

**8.** If you only know the values of $F_g$ and $\theta$, what equation could you use to find $F_{gy}$?

_____

**9.** If you only know the values of $F_g$ and $\theta$, what equation could you use to find $F_{gx}$?

_____

**10.** If the inclined plane is a frictionless surface, what other force aside from those labeled acts on the trunk?

_____

_____

_____

**CHAPTER**

# 5 — Chapter Assessment

# Forces in Two Dimensions

## Understanding Physics Concepts

*Circle the letter of the choice that best completes the statement.*

1. The resultant of a 20-N force acting on an object to the right and a 30-N force acting on the object to the left is _____.

   **a.** 50 N

   **b.** 10 N

   **c.** 10 N acting to the left

   **d.** 30 N acting to the right

2. The equilibrant of a 40-N force acting on an object to the right and a 30-N force acting on the object to the left is _____.

   **a.** 70 N

   **b.** 10 N

   **c.** 10 N acting to the left

   **d.** 10 N acting to the right

3. When adding vectors graphically, one does all the following steps except _____.

   **a.** connect vectors tip-to-tail

   **b.** choose a scale

   **c.** add the components

   **d.** draw the resultant

4. The law of cosines is _____.

   **a.** $R^2 = A^2 + B^2 - 2AB \cos \theta$

   **b.** $\dfrac{\cos A}{A} = \dfrac{\cos B}{B}$

   **c.** $R^2 = A^2 + B^2 + 2AB \cos \theta$

   **d.** $A = A_x + A_y$

5. A graphical representation of a displacement vector of distance $d$ has its tail at the origin of a coordinate system and makes an angle of 30° with the positive $x$-axis. The $x$-component of the vector is _____.

   **a.** $d \cos 30°$

   **b.** $d \sin 30°$

   **c.** $d \tan \theta$

   **d.** $d \cos 60°$

6. The graphical representation of a vector has its tail at the origin of a two-dimensional coordinate system. Both the horizontal and vertical components are negative. The tip of the vector lies in the _____ quadrant.

   **a.** first

   **b.** second

   **c.** third

   **d.** fourth

7. A vector $A$ has $x$- and $y$-components $A_x$ and $A_y$. The angle the vector makes with the $x$-axis is _____.

   **a.** $\tan^{-1} \dfrac{A_x}{A_y}$    **b.** $\tan^{-1} \dfrac{A_y}{A_x}$    **c.** $\tan \dfrac{A_x}{A_y}$    **d.** $\cos^{-1} \dfrac{A_x}{A_y}$

8. The force of kinetic friction between a box sliding on a surface depends on the _____.

   **a.** surface area of the box

   **b.** speed of the box

   **c.** normal force

   **d.** force causing the motion

9. An object at rest on a horizontal surface has a weight of 200 N. In order to move the box a minimum force of 20 N is required. The coefficient of static friction is _____.

   **a.** 10               **b.** 0.10             **c.** greater than 10   **d.** greater than 0.10

10. The coefficient of static friction is _____ the coefficient of kinetic friction.

   **a.** less than         **b.** more than       **c.** equal to         **d.** unrelated to

*Answer the following questions. Show your calculations.*

11. A man walks 400 m in the direction 45° north of east. Represent this vector graphically by selecting a scale and drawing a coordinate system.

12. A force of 500.0 is represented graphically with its tail at the origin and the tip pointed in a direction 30.0° above the positive *x*-axis. What are the *x*- and *y*-components of the vector?

13. A ferry with a velocity of 10.0 m/s travels from one side of the river to the other side at a point directly across. When a current is flowing down the river, the ferry's captain directs the boat at an angle up river so that the ferry arrives at the correct landing point. If the speed of the river water is 2.00 m/s, what is the resultant speed of the ferry?

14. One side of a triangle is 4.0 m and another side is 3.0 m. The angle between the two sides is 142°. What is the length of the third side?

15. One side of a triangle is 4.00 m and another side is 3.00 m. The angle opposite the 4.00-m side is 27.0°. What is the angle opposite the 3.00-m side?

## Thinking Critically

*Answer the following questions. Use complete sentences or show your calculations.*

1. The graphical representation of vector *A* has its tail at the origin and its tip in the first quadrant. Vector *B* has its tail at the origin and its tip in the third quadrant. The resultant *R* of these two vectors is drawn so that its tail is also at the origin. What can you conclude about the location of the tip of the resultant *R*?

   _____

   _____

2. You and your friend are trying without success to push a sofa that is standing on four identical legs to a different location. The bottom of each leg is flat and has an area of 20 cm². Your friend suggests that you get your brother to lift one end of the couch a small distance off the floor so that the area of contact is 40 cm² instead of 80 cm². Your friend argues that this will reduce the force of friction by one half. Is your friend right? Explain your answer.

   _____

   _____

3. A 10-N force is directed along the positive x-axis. A 5-N force is acting in the same direction. What does it mean to subtract the two vectors? Is the result the same whether you subtract the larger vector from the smaller vector or the smaller vector from the larger vector?

   _____

   _____

4. The following three forces act on a single small mass: 50.0 N 30° south of east, 100 N 45° south of west, and 100 N 45° west of north. Using graphical methods, calculate the resultant and equilibrant of these vectors.

*Refer to the passage below to answer questions 5–7.*

> All surfaces, however flat and smooth they appear, are really very rough on a microscopic level. Thus, two surfaces in contact are really in contact at only a few of the high points on each surface. According to a molecular theory of kinetic and static friction, molecules on one surface bond to molecules of the other surface. The force of friction causes these bonds to break so that the two surfaces can move.

**5.** Does the above theory explain why the coefficient of static friction is greater than the coefficient of kinetic friction? Explain your answer.

_____

_____

_____

**6.** Does the above theory explain why the coefficient of kinetic friction does not depend on the speed of the surfaces? Explain.

_____

_____

**7.** Does the above theory explain why the force of friction does not depend on the area of contact? Explain.

_____

_____

## Applying Physics Knowledge

*Answer the following questions. Show your calculations.*

**1.** A box that weighs $5.00 \times 10^2$ N is sliding down a ramp at a constant speed. The angle the ramp makes with the horizontal is 25°. What is the coefficient of friction between the box and the ramp? You may want to draw a free-body diagram to help you solve the problem.

Copyright © Glencoe/McGraw-Hill, a division of The McGraw-Hill Companies, Inc.

**2.** An airplane is traveling 25° west of north at 300 m/s when a wind with velocity 100 m/s directed 35° east of north begins to blow. Using graphical methods, determine the speed and direction of the resultant velocity.

**3.** During a hockey game on a pond, the defenseman passes a 114-g hockey puck over the ice to the center, who fails to catch it. The puck is traveling at an initial speed of 6.7 m/s. It stops in 18 m due to the frictional force on it from the ice.

   **a.** Find the magnitude of the frictional force on the ice.

   **b.** What is the coefficient of kinetic friction between the puck and the ice?

**4.** A sign with a mass of 1000.0 kg is suspended from a wall with a cable that is attached to the wall at a point 3 m above a horizontal beam that causes the sign to be a distance of 4 m from the wall. See the diagram below. What is the tension in the cable? You may want to draw a free-body diagram to help you solve the problem.

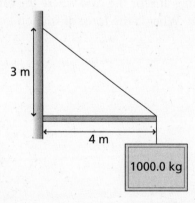

3 m

4 m

1000.0 kg

*Refer to the passage below to answer questions 5–6.*

A dynamical cart used in physics experiments and loaded with weights is pulled at a constant speed up a ramp by a constant force. A spring scale is used to measure the force which is 9.5 N. The cart is then lowered down the ramp at a constant speed by a constant force, which is measured to be 7.0 N.

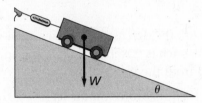

5. In a frame of reference with the *x*-axis parallel to the ramp, draw the free-body diagram showing all the forces acting on the dynamical cart when the cart is being pulled up the ramp. Write the equilibrium condition along the horizontal axis.

6. Likewise, draw the free-body diagram for the case where the cart is being lowered down the ramp. Write the equilibrium equation. What is the force of friction between the cart and the ramp?

# Answer Key

## Chapter 1

### Mini Lab Worksheet

#### Measuring Change

**2.** Student answers will vary depending on the mass of the washers and the spring. However, the graph should show a linear relationship between mass (the number of washers) and the length of the spring.

#### Analyze and Conclude

**5.** Length increases with mass. The line graph should slope up.

### Physics Lab

#### Exploring Objects in Motion

| Marker | Distance (km) | White Vehicle Time (s) | Gray Pickup Time (s) |
|--------|---------------|------------------------|----------------------|
| 0 | 0 | 0 | 0 |
| 1 | 0.322 | 14 | 12 |
| 2 | 0.644 | 28 | 22.5 |

#### Procedure

**3.** Student answers regarding measurements taken will vary, but should include distance and time it takes to travel a certain distance. The camera is in the white vehicle. The pickup truck is gray.

**4.** Students should observe that the road is not smooth, but that it is bumpy. From the direction of the shadow (towards the right), it appears that the vehicles are heading west. See the sample data above for the time it takes each vehicle to travel the two intervals past the white blocks.

#### Analyze

**1.** Answers will vary: Qualitative observations include color, relative speed (for example, fast), bumpy road, partly cloudy.

**2.** Answers will vary. Quantitative observations can include distance along the road between markers, number of vehicles seen, number of lanes, and number of striped lane markers.

**3.** Have students compare their graphs.

**4.** Answers will vary depending on the method used to measure the time for each vehicle to travel the two intervals between markers. Sample:

$$v_{white} = distance/time$$
$$= (0.644 \text{ km}/28.0 \text{ s})(3600 \text{ s/h})$$
$$= 82.8 \text{ km/h}$$
$$v_{grey} = (0.644 \text{ km}/22.5 \text{ s})(3600 \text{ s/h})$$
$$= 103 \text{ km/h}$$

**5.** Answers will vary. Sample:

$$Distance_{white} = speed \times time$$
$$= (0.0230 \text{ km/s})(5 \times 60 \text{ s})$$
$$= 6.90 \text{ km}$$
$$Distance_{gray} = speed \times time$$
$$= (0.0286 \text{ km/s})(5 \times 60 \text{ s})$$
$$= 8.58 \text{ km}$$

#### Conclude and Apply

**1.** Answers will vary. The precision is one-half of the smallest measurement marks. If we assume the distance measurement was done accurately, then it is within $\pm 0.5$ m. The time measurement may be quite different depending on the method used. A stopwatch with one-second increments will produce $\pm 0.5$ second precision, while a built-in timer on video playback software may have a precision of tenths or several hundredths of a second.

**2.** Precision depends on the precision of the measurements and their effect on the results of the calculation. The precision is $\pm 1$ m/s.

3. Dependent variables: time; independent variable: distance
   *Note:* This is reversed from what is typically measured in a speed-finding experiment.

4. The gray vehicle's graph has a steeper slope. The slope is equal to the speed of the vehicle, 28 m/s.

5. A horizontal line would mean that the vehicle is not moving. A line with a steeper slope would mean that the vehicle is traveling faster than the first vehicle.

## Going Further

Answers will vary. Student responses should suggest protocols for ensuring accuracy, such as using evenly spaced markers. As for improving their measurements, rigging a motion detector to a digital chronometer has a far higher degree of accuracy than checking the second hand on a clock face.

## Real-World Physics

Parallax creates the differences. The passenger seats and possibly the rear seat will not provide an accurate view of the speedometer. Looking straight at the speedometer will provide the most accurate reading.

## Share Your Data

Answers will vary. Review student procedures from *Going Further* before posting them.

## Study Guide

### A Physics Toolkit

### Vocabulary Review

1. physics
2. scientific method
3. significant digits
4. inverse relationship
5. line of best fit
6. hypothesis
7. independent variable
8. scientific law
9. measurement
10. linear relationship

11. scientific theory
12. accuracy
13. dependent variable
14. dimensional analysis
15. quadratic relationship
16. precision

## Section 1-1
## Mathematics and Physics

1. experiments
2. experimental data
3. results
4. theories
5. equations
6. units
7. dimensional analysis
8. graphs
9. c
10. e
11. a
12. f
13. h
14. d
15. b
16. i
17. g
18. least
19. three
20. with the number of significant digits required by the problem
21. 2
22. 1
23. 3
24. This can best be described as an observation because you have noticed a natural phenomenon.
25. The fact that exact units are mentioned makes this a quantitative measurement.
26. This statement describes the summing up of observations into a scientific law.
27. This is a hypothesis or prediction based on previous experience.
28. This is an example of reproducing results because you are doing the experiment a second time.

**29.** This is a scientific theory based on many observations and supported by experimental results.

## Section 1-2
## Measurement

**1.** a

**2.** c

**3.** d

**4.** b

**5.** c

**6.** a

**7.** d

## Section 1-3
## Graphing Data

**1.** quadratic

**2.** The dependent variable is time and the independent variable is distance.

**3.** positive

**4.** $\dfrac{m}{s}$

**5.** The graph is steeper at 2.0 s than at 1.0 s.

**6.** 15 m

**7.** $d = 5t^2$

$\quad = 5(2.4)^2$

$\quad = 28$

The distance is 28 m

**8.** inverse

**9.** negative

**10.** ohms/A

**11.** 5 A

**12.** $I = \dfrac{k}{A}$

**13.** d

**14.** c

**15.** f

**16.** a

**17.** e

**18.** b

## Section 1-1 Quiz

**1.** Physicists communicate with other scientists from all over the world. Making research understandable to all is important for the progress of science. All scientists understand SI units.

**2.** The steps are to define the problem, make a hypothesis, conduct experiments, collect data, and create explanations.

**3.** Significant digits are the valid digits in a measurement. For example, if you measure a pencil and find that it is 12.5 cm long, all three digits are significant. However, the last digit is uncertain because it is at the limit of your measuring instrument. The pencil could really be 12.54 cm long, but the measurer cannot determine that due to the limits of the equipment. Zero can be a significant digit in a measurement such as 26.50 m because it is the estimated (possibly uncertain) digit. However, the zeros are not significant in the measurement 0.0079 m because the number could be rewritten as $7.9 \times 10^{-3}$. The zeros are only in the measurement to fix the location of the decimal point.

**4.** $v = at$

$t = \dfrac{v}{a}$

$\quad = \dfrac{5 \text{ m/s}}{0.5 \text{ m/s}^2}$

$\quad = 10 \text{ s}$

## Section 1-2 Quiz

**1.** Precision is the degree of exactness of a measurement. Precision is limited by the number of divisions on the measuring tool. A measurement can only be precise to one-half of the smallest division of the instrument. Accuracy refers to a comparison between a measuring instrument and a standard. Scientists calibrate their instruments to verify that they maintain their accuracy.

**2.** Every measured value has some level of uncertainty. For example, the equipment measuring the radiocarbon dates of cave paintings are accurate within 600 years because that is the limit of the measuring technology. If another scientific group wanted to date the cave paintings and got a similar result accurate within 600 years, the two groups of results would confirm each other.

**3. a.** The third measurement is the most precise. It has the lowest variation.

   **b.** The second measurement is the most accurate. It is closest to the actual value.

**4. a.** (7.4 cm)(8.3 cm) = 61 cm$^2$

   **b.** The measurements are precise to 0.5 mm because the precision of a measuring device is one-half the smallest division of the device.

## Section 1-3 Quiz

**1.** Possible answer: When numbers are plotted on a graph, trends and relationships become more obvious than they were in table form. For example, when numbers have an inverse relationship, the resulting graph takes the form of a hyperbola. A knowledgeable mathematician would understand this just by looking at the picture of the results.

**2.** Slope is the ratio of vertical change (rise) to horizontal change (run). You can calculate the slope of any linear graph. To calculate a slope, find two distant points (A and B) along the y-axis (rise) and subtract them. Divide this result by the difference between points A and B along the x-axis (run).

**3.** $m = \dfrac{\text{rise}}{\text{run}} = \dfrac{\Delta y}{\Delta x}$

$= \dfrac{6.5\ \text{g} - 4.6\ \text{g}}{3.3\ \text{mL} - 5.9\ \text{mL}}$

$= -0.73\ \text{g/mL}$

**4.** $d = 7t^2 + 27$

$= 7(6.00)^2 + 27$

$= 279$

The distance is 279 m.

## Chapter 1 Reinforcement

### Determining Relationships from Graphs

**Procedure**

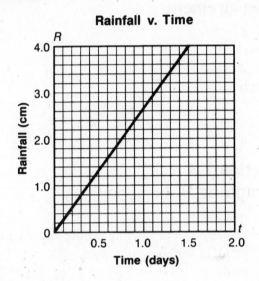

**Rainfall v. Time**

**1.** $m = \dfrac{\Delta y}{\Delta x}$

$\dfrac{\Delta y}{\Delta x} = \dfrac{y_2 - y_1}{x_2 - x_1}$

$m = \dfrac{2.6\ \text{cm} - 0.0\ \text{cm}}{10\ \text{days} - 0.0\ \text{days}}$

$= 2.6\ \text{cm/day}$

**2.** The y-intercept is 0.0

**3.** $R = (2.7\ \text{cm/day})t$

**4.** No. Even with no rainfall, the graph would be a straight line running along the x-axis with a slope of 0.

**5.** If more rainfall falls over the same period of time, the slope of the graph is steeper.

## Chapter 1 Enrichment

### Graphing Nonlinear Relationships

#### Procedure

| Time (s) | Distance (m) |
|----------|--------------|
| 1        | 4.90         |
| 2        | 19.6         |
| 3        | 44.1         |
| 4        | 78.4         |
| 5        | 122          |
| 6        | 176          |
| 7        | 240          |
| 8        | 313          |
| 9        | 397          |
| 10       | 490          |

#### Results

1. The independent variable is time. The dependent variable is distance because the distance the object falls depends on elapsed time.

2.

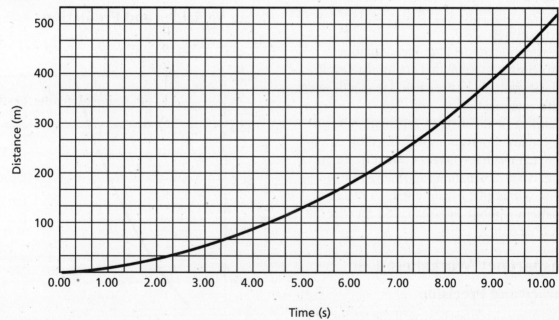

3. The graph is a parabola because Galileo's equation is a quadratic relationship in which one variable depends on the square of another.

## Transparency Worksheet 1-1

### Dimensional Analysis

1. The two base quantities used to measure speed are length and time.

2. The value of a conversion factor, by definition, is always one because the quantities in the numerator and denominator are equal. It is important that a conversion factor be equal to one because the conversion factor cannot affect the value of the number being converted, it can only change its units.

3. $(1 \text{ s})\left(\dfrac{1 \text{ min}}{60 \text{ s}}\right)\left(\dfrac{1 \text{ h}}{60 \text{ min}}\right) = \dfrac{1}{3600} \text{ h}$

So, 1 s is equal to $\dfrac{1}{3600}$ h. In other words, there are 3600 s in 1 h. Thus, a conversion factor to convert seconds directly to hours is $\dfrac{1 \text{ h}}{3600 \text{ s}}$.

**4.** $(22.2 \text{ m/s})\left(\dfrac{60 \text{ s}}{1 \text{ min}}\right)\left(\dfrac{60 \text{ min}}{1 \text{ h}}\right)\left(\dfrac{1 \text{ km}}{1000 \text{ m}}\right)$
$= 79.9 \text{ km/h}$

**5.** $(22.2 \text{ m/s})\left(\dfrac{3600 \text{ s}}{1 \text{ h}}\right)\left(\dfrac{1 \text{ km}}{1000 \text{ m}}\right) = 79.9 \text{ km/h}$

## Transparency Worksheet 1-2

### Scientific Methods

**1.** Observation is the foundation for any scientific method and every step of a scientific method must refer to the observations that have been made. Hypotheses, scientific laws, and scientific theories all rely on observation for validation. In other words, the scientific process begins with observation when a scientist observes something he or she wants to further investigate, and the scientific process is maintained by observation as scientists compare what they are able to observe to whatever scientific model or theory is most current.

**2.** A scientific law is a rule of nature that sums up related observations to describe a pattern in nature. Some examples of scientific laws are the law of conservation of energy, the law of conservation of charge, and the law of reflection.

**3.** A scientific model is an idea, equation, structure, or system that attempts to explain the current data on a particular area of scientific investigation.

**4.** A scientific theory is an explanation based on many observations supported by experimental results. Whereas a scientific theory offers an explanation for observed phenomena, a scientific law only states a rule or a pattern without an explanation for why the rule or pattern exists.

## Transparency Worksheet 1-3

### Accuracy and Precision

**1.** Accuracy describes how well the results of a measurement agree with the accepted or real value.

**2.** Precision is the degree of exactness of a mea-

surement. For instance, a measurement that measures to the closest thousandth of an inch is more precise than a measurement that measures to the nearest tenth of an inch.

**3.** Figure a provides the best representation of accuracy without precision. The arrow hit the center of the target, or the real value, but without other arrows, it is impossible to know how narrow of a range the measurement is capable of producing. Thus, the precision of the measurement is subject to doubt.

**4.** Figure b is the best representation of precision without accuracy. Although none of the measurements are close to the center or real value, they are all grouped very close together, indicating that the exactness of the measurement is high.

**5.** Figure c is the best representation of accuracy and precision. The arrows all hit the center and are thus accurate. Also they are also grouped close together, which indicates that the measurement has a high degree of exactness, or accuracy, and thus a high degree of precision.

## Transparency Worksheet 1-4

### Using Variables and Predicting

**1.**

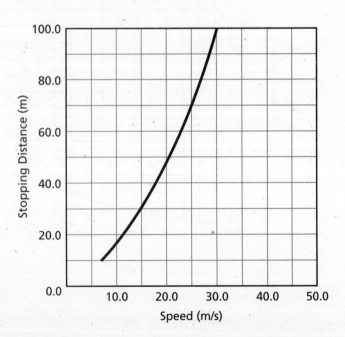

**2.** The independent variable is the factor that is changed or manipulated during an experiment. A dependent variable is the condition that is controlled by the independent variable.

**3.** The independent variable is speed and the dependent variable is stopping distance.

**4.** The relationship between speed and stopping distance is quadratic.

**5.** The curve indicates that the relationship between the variables is a positive quadratic relationship. Therefore, as speed increases beyond 30 m/s, the braking distance will increase at an ever-increasing rate.

# Chapter 1 Chapter Assessment

## A Physics Toolkit

### Understanding Physics Concepts

**1.** c

**2.** b

**3.** a

**4.** d

**5.** d

**6.** true

**7.** precision

**8.** true

**9.** uncertain

**10.** beginning

**11.** Physicists do experiments, make observations, record data, and use the data to create models or theories to answer questions.

**12.** Possible answers include telecommunications satellites, telescopes, and computers.

**13.** Because the millimeter is the smaller unit, the length of the tabletop measured in millimeters is more precise.

**14.** 88.5 cm, 88.40 cm

**15.** **a.** 4

   **b.** 4

   **c.** 2

**16.** Precision is the degree of exactness used in measuring a quantity. Accuracy is the extent to which the measured value of a quantity agrees with the real value.

## Thinking Critically

**1.** d

**2.** a

**3.** b

**4.** c

**5.** d

**6.** c

**7.** c

**8.** true

**9.** quadratic

**10.** true

**11.** independent

**12.** true

**13.** linear

**14.** **a.** $1.42 \times 10^5$ s

   **b.** $8.09 \times 10^{-3}$ kg

   **c.** $5.01 \times 10^8$ m

**15.** **a.** $1 \times 10^{12}$ m$^2$

   **b.** $3 \times 10^4$ m/s

   **c.** 8.630 km

**16.** The graph shows an inverse relationship between time and speed. $y = \dfrac{a}{x}$

## Applying Physics Knowledge

**1.** The only measurement with zeros that are not significant is 0.0053m; the zeros are used solely to locate the decimal point. In all the other measurements, the zeros after the decimal point are significant.

**2.** The independent variable is a manipulated variable. It is graphed on the x-axis. A dependent variable changes due to a change in the independent variable. It is plotted on the y-axis.

**3.** D = 5.000 kg − A − B − C
   = 5.000 kg − 0.000256 kg −
                    0.05117 kg − 0.382 kg
   = 4.567 kg

**4.** 5687 nm = $(5.687 \times 10^3$ nm$)\left(\dfrac{1 \text{ m}}{10^9 \text{ nm}}\right)$
                    = $5.687 \times 10^{-6}$ m
   0.00005687 dm =
   $(5.687 \times 10^{-5}$ dm$)\left(\dfrac{1 \text{ m}}{10 \text{ dm}}\right) = 5.687 \times 10^{-6}$ m

**5. a.**

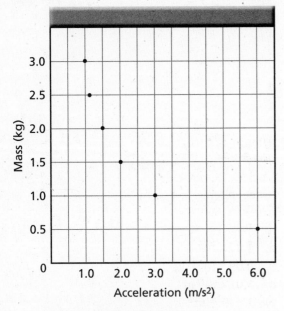

Mass (kg) vs Acceleration (m/s²)

**b.** The graph is a hyperbola.

**c.** The relationship between the variables is inverse.

**d.** $a = \dfrac{k}{m}$, where $k$ is a constant, $m$ is mass, and $a$ is acceleration.

**6.** $\left(\dfrac{86\ km}{1\ h}\right)\left(\dfrac{1000\ m}{1\ km}\right)\left(\dfrac{1\ h}{60\ m}\right)\left(\dfrac{1\ min}{60\ s}\right) =$

$24\ m/s$

# Chapter 2

## Mini Lab Worksheet

### Instantaneous Velocity Vectors

#### Analyze and Conclude

**6.**

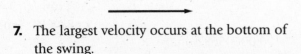

**7.** The largest velocity occurs at the bottom of the swing.

**8.** The velocity at the top is equal to zero, while the mass is at rest momentarily. A dot may be used to indicate the velocity at this point.

**9.** The magnitude of the speed is equal to the magnitude of the velocity vectors halfway between the highest and lowest points. Students may suggest adding the magnitudes of the fastest and slowest speeds and dividing the sum in half.

## Physics Lab Worksheet

### Creating Motion Diagrams

Data Table 1

| Time (s) | Car #1 Location (cm) |
|----------|----------------------|
| 0.0 | 11 |
| 0.1 | 13 |
| 0.2 | 14 |
| 0.3 | 16 |
| 0.4 | 18 |
| 0.5 | 19 |

Data Table 2

| Time (s) | Car #2 Location (cm) |
|----------|----------------------|
| 0.0 | 16 |
| 0.1 | 19 |
| 0.2 | 23 |
| 0.3 | 26 |
| 0.4 | 30 |
| 0.5 | 34 |

#### Analyze

**1.** ⟶ ⟶ ⟶ ⟶

**2.** ⟶ ⟶ ⟶ ⟶ ⟶

**3.** ⟶ ⟶ ⟶ ⟶ ⟶

#### Conclude and Apply

A fast car has arrows that are farther apart, while a slow car has arrows that are closer together.

#### Going Further

**1.** ⟶ ⟶ ⟶ ⟶

**2.** In the motion diagram of a car moving at constant speed, the distances between points are equal.

**3.**

**4.** In the motion diagram of a car that is slowing down, the distances between the points become shorter as the car slows—*i.e.*, the points are closer together.

**5.** ►─►─►──►───►────►

**6.** In the motion diagram of a car that is speeding up, the distances between points become longer as the car goes faster *i.e.*, the points are farther apart.

### Real-World Physics

The tread marks should appear to be shorter as the driver of the car applies the brakes.

## Chapter 2 Study Guide

### Representing Motion

### Vocabulary Review

1. instantaneous velocity
2. magnitude
3. position
4. time interval
5. vector
6. average velocity
7. coordinate system
8. origin
9. position time graph
10. motion diagram
11. resultant
12. particle model
13. distance
14. scalar
15. instantaneous position
16. displacement
17. average speed

## Section 2.1
## Picturing Motion

1. B
2. B
3. D
4. C
5. A

## Section 2.2
## Where and When?

1. 4 m, −4 m, 5 m, 3 m, and 0 m
2. 1 m/s
3. −1 m/s
4. A, C, D
5. B

## Section 2.3
## Position-Time Graphs

1. time
2. position
3. 9.0 m
4. 4.0 s
5. 1.5 m/s
6. $\bar{v} = \dfrac{\Delta d}{\Delta t}$

$\Delta t = \dfrac{\Delta d}{\bar{v}}$

$= \dfrac{18.0\ \text{m}}{1.5\ \text{m/s}}$

$= 12\ \text{s}$

7. $\bar{v} = \dfrac{\Delta d}{\Delta t}$

$\Delta d = \bar{v}\Delta t$

$= (1.5\ \text{m/s})(300\ \text{s})$

$= 400\ \text{m}$

## Section 2.4
## How Fast?

1. $\Delta t = t_f - t_i$
2. at $d = 15.0$ m, $t_f = 6.0$ s
   at $d = 5.0$ m, $t_i = 2.0$ s
   $\Delta t = t_f - t_i$
   $= 6.0\ \text{s} - 2.0\ \text{s}$
   $= 4.0\ \text{s}$
3. $\Delta d = d_f - d_i$
4. at $t = 8$ s, $d_f = 20.0$ m
   at $t = 2$ s, $d_i = 5.0$ m
   $\Delta d = d_f - d_i$
   $= 20.0\ \text{m} - 5.0\ \text{m}$
   $= 15.0\ \text{m}$
5. $v = \dfrac{d_f - d_i}{t_f - t_i}$

**6.** $v = \dfrac{d_f - d_i}{t_f - t_i}$

$= \dfrac{(20.0 \text{ m} - 0.0 \text{ m})}{(8.0 \text{ s} - 0.0 \text{ s})}$

$= 2.5 \text{ m/s}$

**7.** average speed

**8.** $+2.5 \text{ m/s}$

**9.** $\bar{v} = \dfrac{\Delta d}{\Delta t}$

$\Delta t = \dfrac{\Delta d}{\bar{v}}$

$= \dfrac{150 \text{ m}}{2.5 \text{ m/s}}$

$= 6.0 \times 10^1 \text{ s}$

**10.** $\bar{v} = \dfrac{\Delta d}{\Delta t}$

$\Delta d = \bar{v}\Delta t$

$= (2.5 \text{ m/s})(200 \text{ s})$

$= 500 \text{ m}$

**11.** $d = vt + d_i$

**12.** $d = vt + d_i$

$= (2.5 \text{ m/s})(48 \text{ s}) + 220 \text{ m}$

$= 340 \text{ m}$

## Section 2.1 Quiz

1. A motion diagram is a series of images that show the positions of a moving object at equal time intervals.
2. The particle model is a motion diagram in which the object has been replaced by a series of single points. The particle model is simpler than the motion diagram.
3. Place and time.
4. Answers will vary greatly. Some examples are the movement of a small child across the playground, a jogger traveling on a straight path, or a car traveling down a straight street.

## Section 2.2 Quiz

1. A vector has both magnitude and direction, while a scalar only has magnitude.
2. A resultant is the sum of two or more vectors.

**3.** $\Delta d = d_f - d_i$

If the student's starting point is defined as zero, the equation becomes

$\Delta d = d_f$

Thus, the student's displacement is equal to his or her final position and the final position is equal to the sum of all of the displacements. So,

$\Delta d = d_1 + d_2 + d_3$

$\Delta d = (4 \text{ blocks N}) + (9 \text{ blocks N}) +$

$\phantom{\Delta d = } (6 \text{ blocks N})$

$\Delta d = 19 \text{ blocks N}$

**4.**

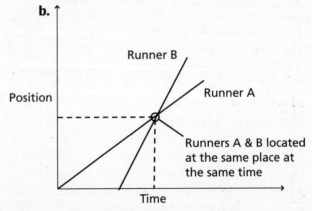

6 km West

6 km South     6 km North

6 km East

Starting Point

$\Delta d = 0 \text{ km}$

## Section 2.3 Quiz

1. Time is represented on the *x*-axis and position is represented on the *y*-axis.
2. The object the graph represents is not moving.
3. This is unlikely, as this would represent an object moving at an infinite speed.
4. **a.** They are in the same place at the same time.

   **b.**

Runner B

Runner A

Position

Runners A & B located at the same place at the same time

Time

**5.** The objects are in the same place at the same time, but they are not necessarily in collision. All that is known is that their position with reference to the origin is the same.

## Quiz Section 2.4

**1.** Speed does not contain a direction component and velocity does. In other words, speed is a scalar quantity and velocity is a vector quantity.

**2.** Average velocity is the total distance traveled divided by the total time of travel. Instantaneous velocity is the velocity at one given instant. An example of instantaneous velocity is the velocity recorded by a police radar gun. An example of average velocity is a 120-mile car trip that takes 2 hours so that the average velocity was 60 mph.

**3.** $v$ is velocity in m/s, $t$ is time in s, and $d$ is distance in m.

**4.** $\bar{v} = \dfrac{\Delta d}{\Delta t}$

$= \dfrac{450 \text{ km}}{9.0 \text{ h}}$

$= 5.0 \times 10^1 \text{ km/h}$

**5.** $\bar{v} = \dfrac{\Delta d}{\Delta t}$

$\Delta d = \bar{v}\Delta t$

$= (30 \text{ m/s})(3.0 \times 10^2 \text{ s})$

$= 9000 \text{ m}$

## Reinforcement

**1.** $\bar{v} = \dfrac{\Delta d}{\Delta t}$

$\Delta d = \bar{v}\Delta t$

$\Delta d = (55 \text{ km/h})(60 \text{ h})$

$\Delta d = 330 \text{ km}$

**2.** $\bar{v} = \dfrac{\Delta d}{\Delta t}$

$\bar{v} = \dfrac{2500 \text{ km}}{22 \text{ h}}$

$\bar{v} = 1.1 \times 10^3 \text{ km/h}$

**3.** $\bar{v} = \dfrac{\Delta d}{\Delta t}$

$\Delta t = \dfrac{\Delta d}{\bar{v}}$

$\Delta t = \dfrac{11 \text{ km}}{18 \text{ km/h}}$

$= 0.61 \text{ h} = 37 \text{ min}$

**4.** $d = v_t + d_i$

$= (75 \text{ km/h})(8.0 \text{ h}) + 350 \text{ km}$

$= 950 \text{ km}$

**5.** $\Delta d_{total} = \Delta d_{day1} + \Delta d_{day2} + \Delta d_{day3}$

$\Delta d_{day3} = \Delta d_{total} - (\Delta d_{day1} + \Delta d_{day2})$

$\Delta t_{day3} = \dfrac{\Delta d_{day3}}{v_{day3}}$

$\Delta t_{day3} = \dfrac{\Delta d_{total} - (\Delta d_{day1} + \Delta d_{day2})}{v_{day3}}$

$\Delta t_{day3} = \dfrac{23{,}000 \text{ km} - (4{,}000 \text{ km} + 11{,}000 \text{ km})}{570 \text{ km/h}}$

$\Delta t_{day3} = 10 \text{ h}$

## Enrichment

### Instantaneous Velocity

**1.** $\bar{v} = \dfrac{\Delta d}{\Delta t}$

$\Delta t = \dfrac{\Delta d}{\bar{v}}$

$= \dfrac{4800 \text{ km}}{120 \text{ km/h}}$

$= 4.0 \times 10^1 \text{ h}$

**2.** $\bar{v} = \dfrac{\Delta d}{\Delta t}$

$\Delta t = \dfrac{\Delta d}{\bar{v}}$

$= \dfrac{150{,}000 \text{ km}}{110 \text{ km/h}}$

$= 1.4 \times 10^3 \text{ h}$

**3.** $d = v_t + d_i$

$= (65 \text{ km/h})(72 \text{ h}) +$
$\quad\quad (1800 \text{ km} + 2100 \text{ km})$

$= 8.6 \times 10^3 \text{ km}$

**4.** $d = v_t + d_i$

$t = \dfrac{d - d_i}{v}$

$= \dfrac{4100 \text{ km} - (1500 \text{ km} + 1200 \text{ km})}{120 \text{ km/h}}$

$= 12 \text{ hrs}$

**5.** $\bar{v} = \dfrac{\Delta d}{\Delta t}$

$v_A = \dfrac{1200 \text{ km}}{8.0 \text{ h}} = 150 \text{ km/h}$

$v_B = \dfrac{1100 \text{ km}}{6.5 \text{ h}} = 170 \text{ km/h}$

$v_C = \dfrac{1300 \text{ km}}{8.3 \text{ h}} = 160 \text{ km/h}$

Car B is the fastest and car A is the slowest.

$t_A = \dfrac{\Delta d_B}{\Delta v_A}$

$= \dfrac{1100 \text{ km}}{150 \text{ km/h}}$

$= 7.3 \text{ h}$

**6.** $\bar{v} = \dfrac{\Delta d}{\Delta t}$

$\Delta t = \dfrac{\Delta d}{\bar{v}}$

$= \dfrac{780 \text{ km}}{65 \text{ km/h}}$

$= 12 \text{ h}$

avg. mileage $= \dfrac{780 \text{ km}}{53 \text{ L}} = 15 \text{ km/L}$

**7.** $\bar{v} = \dfrac{\Delta d}{\Delta t}$

$\Delta d = \bar{v}\Delta t$

$\dfrac{\Delta d}{L} = \dfrac{\bar{v}\Delta t}{L}$

$\dfrac{\bar{v}_A \Delta t_A}{L} = \dfrac{(120 \text{ km/h})(42 \text{ h})}{45 \text{ L}} = 11 \text{ km/L}$

$\dfrac{\bar{v}_B \Delta t_B}{L} = \dfrac{(120 \text{ km/h})(54 \text{ h})}{45 \text{ L}} = 14 \text{ km/L}$

**8.** $L_f = 45 - \Delta d_{driven}\left(\dfrac{45 \text{ L}}{\Delta d_{total}}\right)$

$L_f = 45 - \bar{v}\Delta t_{driven}\left(\dfrac{45 \text{ L}}{\bar{v}\Delta t_{total}}\right)$

$L_f = 45 -$

$\quad (120 \text{ km/h})(5 \text{ h})\left(\dfrac{45 \text{ L}}{(120 \text{ km/h})(5.4 \text{ h})}\right)$

$L_f = 3 \text{ L}$

$L = \Delta d\left(\dfrac{45 \text{ L}}{\bar{v}\Delta t}\right)$

$L = (1200 \text{ km})\left(\dfrac{45 \text{ L}}{(120 \text{ km/h})(54 \text{ h})}\right) = 83 \text{ L}$

$83 \text{ L} - 45 \text{ L} = 38 \text{ L}$

4 gas cans are needed

## Transparency Worksheet 2-1

### Motion Diagrams

**1.** $v$, $d$, and $t$

**2.** $\Delta d = d_1 - d_0$

**3.** $\Delta d = 50 \text{ m} - 0 \text{ m} = 50 \text{ m}$

**4.** $\Delta t = t_1 - t_0$

**5.** $\Delta t = 6 \text{ s} - 0 \text{ s} = 6 \text{ s}$

**6.** $\bar{v} = \dfrac{50 \text{ m}}{6 \text{ s}} = 8 \text{ m/s}$

**7.** $v$ is proportional to $\Delta d$ because $\Delta t$ is constant.

**8.** $d = \bar{v}t + d_i$

$t + d_i = \dfrac{d}{\bar{v}}$

$t = \dfrac{d}{\bar{v} - d_i}$

$= \dfrac{100 \text{ m}}{8.3 \text{ m/s}} - 0 \text{ m}$

$= 12 \text{ s}$

or 10 s to one significant digit

## Transparency Worksheet 2-2

### Vector Addition

**1.** $120 \text{ km/h} + 30 \text{ km/h} = 150 \text{ km/h}$ north

**2.**

120 km/h

30 km/h

**3.** $120 \text{ km/h} - 30 \text{ km/h} = 90 \text{ km/h}$ north

# Answer Key

**4.**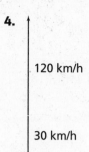

120 km/h

30 km/h

## Transparency Worksheet 2-3

### Vector Subtraction

1. A scalar is a quantity that is just a number without any direction, such as distance, time, or temperature. A vector is a quantity that has both direction and size (or magnitude).

2. At the tip of vector A, draw a vector $-B$. Vector $-B$ has the same magnitude as vector $B$, but the opposite direction. Then draw a vector from the tail of vector $A$ to the tip of vector $-B$. This new vector is the subtraction product.

3. The vector for her overall movement is a vector showing movement 3 km due east.

4. **a.** $d_i = 20$ km north
   **b.** $d_f = 100$ km north
   **c.** $\Delta d = d_f + (-d_i)$
   $= 100$ km north $+ (-20$ km north$)$
   $= 80$ km north

5. The magnitude and direction of $\Delta d$ would be 80 km north. The displacement of the car does not depend on the starting point.

## Transparency Worksheet 2-4

### Position v. Time

1. Time is the independent variable. Position is the dependent variable.

2. Graph A represents a linear relationship. Graph B represents a parabolic relationship.

3. $m = \dfrac{d_f - d_i}{t_f - t_i}$

$= \dfrac{100.0 \text{ m} - 0.0 \text{ m}}{5.0 \text{ s} - 0.0 \text{ s}}$

$= 2.0 \times 10^1$ m/s

The slope represents the average velocity.

4. $\Delta d = d_f - d_i$
   $= 100.0 \text{ m} - 60.0 \text{ m}$
   $= 40.0 \text{ m}$

5. $d = \bar{v}t - d_i$
   $= (20.0 \text{ m/s})(10 \text{ s}) - 0.0 \text{ m}$
   $= 200 \text{ m}$

6. $\Delta d_{1.0/0.0} = 10.0 \text{ m} - 0.0 \text{ m}$
   $= 10.0 \text{ m}$
   $\Delta d_{2.0/1.0} = 40.0 \text{ m} - 10.0 \text{ m}$
   $= 30.0 \text{ m}$
   10.0 m, 30.0 m. The velocity of the object is increasing.

7. In graph A, the velocity is constant. In graph B, the velocity is increasing.

8. They are at the same position at 0.0 s and 2.0 s. At 0.0 s, they are both at 0.0 m; at 2.0 s, they are both at 40.0 m.

9. $\bar{v} = \dfrac{\Delta d}{\Delta t}$

$= \dfrac{d_2 - d_1}{t_2 - t_1}$

$= \dfrac{90.0 \text{ m} - 0.0 \text{ m}}{3.0 \text{ s} - 0.0 \text{ s}}$

$= 3.0 \times 10^1$ m/s

## Chapter Assessment

### Understanding Physics Concepts

1. c
2. q
3. g
4. e
5. k
6. o
7. d
8. m
9. h
10. a
11. j
12. f

**13.** i

**14.** n

**15.** l

**16.** p

**17.** b

**18.** True

**19.** times

**20.** magnitude

**21.** origin

**22.** true

**23.** c

**24.** c

**25.** a

**26.** d

**27.** c

**28.** b

## Thinking Critically

**1.** $3 \times 10^2$ m

**2.** 30 m/s

**3. a.** $\Delta t = t_f - t_i$
$$= 4.0 \text{ s} - 0.0 \text{ s}$$
$$= 4.0 \text{ s}$$

**b.** $\bar{v} = \dfrac{\Delta d}{\Delta t}$

$$\bar{v} = \frac{80.0 \text{ m} - 0.0 \text{ m}}{5.0 \text{ s} - 0.0 \text{ s}}$$

$$\bar{v} = 16 \text{ s}$$

**c.** The 3-4 interval covers 10.0 m, the 4–5 interval covers 40.0 m.

**d.** They are the same.

**e.**

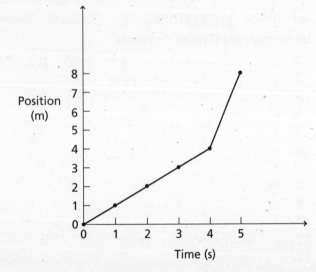

**4.**
$$\bar{v} = \frac{v_{1st-half} + v_{2nd-half}}{2}$$

$$v_{2nd-half} = 2\bar{v} - v_{1st-half}$$
$$= 2(24 \text{ km/h}) - 21 \text{ km/h}$$
$$= 27 \text{ km/h}$$

**5. a.** $\Delta t = \dfrac{\Delta d}{v}$

$$= \frac{7.0 \times 10^1 \text{ km}}{21 \text{ km/h}} = 3.3 \text{ h}$$

**b.** $\Delta t = \dfrac{\Delta d}{\bar{v}}$

$$= \frac{7.0 \times 10^1 \text{ km}}{25 \text{ km/h}} = 2.8 \text{ h}$$

2.8 h + 3.3 h = 6.1 h

Destination will not be reached in time

**c.** $\bar{v} = \dfrac{\Delta d}{\Delta t}$,

where $\Delta t = 6.0 \text{ h} - \dfrac{7.0 \times 10^1 \text{ km}}{21 \text{ km/h}}$

$$\bar{v} = \frac{7.0 \times 10^1 \text{ km}}{\left( 6.0 \text{ h} - \dfrac{7.0 \times 10^1 \text{ km}}{21 \text{ km/h}} \right)}$$

$$= 26 \text{ km/h}$$

**d.**

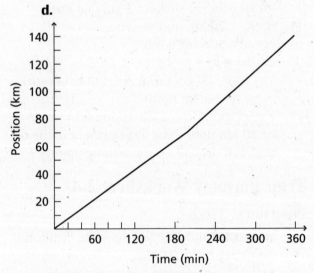

## Applying Physics Knowledge

**1.** You can compare the location of the object to other objects in the frame that are stationary.

**2.** The object can have a negative position if it is on the opposite side of the origin than the side that has been designated as positive.

**3.** The object is moving back in forth in such a manner that it appears in the same position in successive frames.

**4.** This means that the object is moving at 15 m/s in the positive direction relative to the origin in the coordinate system.

**5.** 1 light year is the distance light travels in a year so it will take 6.45 yr.

$$(6.45 \text{ y})\left(\frac{365 \text{ days}}{\text{y}}\right)\left(\frac{25 \text{ h}}{\text{day}}\right)$$

$$\left(\frac{3600 \text{ s}}{\text{h}}\right)\left(\frac{3.00 \times 10^8 \text{ m}}{\text{s}}\right) = 6.10 \times 10^{16} \text{ m}$$

**6.** Relative to runner A, runner B's velocity is
$$v_B - v_A = 7.90 \text{ m/s} - 7.50 \text{ m/s} = 0.4 \text{ m/s}$$

$$\Delta t = \frac{\Delta d}{\overline{v}}$$

$$= \frac{55.0 \text{ m}}{04 \text{ m/s}} = 100 \text{ s}$$

**7.** $\Delta d = v\Delta t$
$$= (309 \text{ m/s})(1.21 \text{ s})$$
$$= 374 \text{ m}$$

**8.** $t_{total} = t_1 + t_2 + t_3$
$$t_{total} = \frac{\Delta d_1}{v_1} + \frac{\Delta d_2}{v_2} + \frac{\Delta d_3}{v_3}$$

$$= \frac{52 \text{ m}}{24 \text{ m/s}} + \frac{79 \text{ m}}{12 \text{ m/s}} + \frac{25 \text{ m}}{34 \text{ m/s}}$$

$$= 95 \text{ s}$$

**9.** Since he is paddling against the current, his velocity relative to the shore will be
$$v_{canoe} - v_{current} =$$
$$6.2 \text{ m/s} - 6.1 \text{ m/s} = 0.1 \text{ m/s}$$
Since his velocity relative to the shore is positive, he is making headway at a speed of 0.1 m/s.

# Chapter 3

## Mini Lab

### Analyze and Conclude

**6.** In Step 4, the instantaneous velocities of the balls are equal. At each moment in Step 5, the velocity of the second ball is greater than that of the first.

**7.** The distance between the balls remains the same in Step 4 because at each moment the velocities of both balls are equal and are apparently increasing at the same rate. In step 5 the distance between the two balls increases because at each moment the velocity of the first ball is greater than that of the second and both velocities are apparently increasing at the same rate. (The distance between the two balls, $d_{1-2}$, is give by the equation $d_{1-2} = d + (\sqrt{2ad})(t)$, where $d$ is the distance between the two balls when the second ball is released (0.40 m), a is the acceleration down the incline, and $t$ is the time that the second ball has been moving.)

**8.** One can infer from the observations of Step 4 that the balls have the same acceleration.

## Physics Lab

### Sample Data

Timer period (#/s) = 1/60 s

| Interval | Distance (cm) | Time (s) | Distance/Time (cm/s) |
|----------|---------------|----------|----------------------|
| 1 | 1.6 | 1/60 | 96 |
| 2 | 3.4 | 2/60 | $1.0 \times 10^2$ |
| 3 | 5.6 | 3/60 | $1.0 \times 10^2$ |
| 4 | 8.0 | 4/60 | $1.2 \times 10^2$ |
| 5 | 10.6 | 5/60 | 127 |
| 6 | 13.6 | 6/60 | 136 |
| 7 | 16.9 | 7/60 | 145 |
| 8 | 20.3 | 8/60 | 152 |
| 9 | 24.1 | 9/60 | 161 |
| 10 | 28.1 | 10/60 | 169 |
| 11 | 32.5 | 11/60 | 177 |
| 12 | 37.0 | 12/60 | 185 |
| 13 | 41.9 | 13/60 | 193 |

## Analyze

1. See sample data table.
2.

3. Sample slope

$$= \frac{192.4 \text{ cm/s} - 112 \text{ cm/s}}{13/60 \text{ s} - 3/60 \text{ s}}$$

$$= 482 \text{ cm/s}^2$$

$$= 4.82 \text{ m/s}^2$$

## Conclude and Apply

1. $g = (2)(4.82 \text{ m/s}^2)$
   $= 9.64 \text{ m/s}^2$

2. % error
   $$= \frac{9.80 \text{ m/s}^2 - 9.64 \text{ m/s}^2}{9.80 \text{ m/s}^2} \times 100 = 1.63\%$$

3. From $y$-intercept of graph, $v_i = 0.83$ m/s.

## Going Further

Answers will vary. Possible answers may include: that error was reduced by not having to use the beginning of the timer tape, which may have jerked when it was first dropped; the dots may be very close together at the beginning, making it difficult to accurately count; or there may have been a lag in time from when the dot was made and when the mass was dropped at rest, creating a small error.

## Real-World Physics

The curved section gradually reduces the acceleration along the curve. The acceleration along the straight portion of the exit track is negative and causes the rapidly moving cart to slow. Both sections prevent a sudden decrease in velocity of the cart, which might cause injuries to its passengers.

# Chapter 3 Study Guide

## Vocabulary Review

1. velocity-time graph
2. instantaneous acceleration
3. acceleration
4. free fall
5. average acceleration
6. acceleration due to gravity

# Section 3.1
# Acceleration

1.

| Segment | $v$ | $\Delta t$ | $\Delta d$ |
|---------|-----|-----------|-----------|
| A | 0.25 km/min | 10.0 min | 2.5 km |
| B | 0.0 km/min | 7.0 min | 0.0 km |
| C | 0.40 km/min | 13.0 min | 5.2 km |

| $\Delta t$ | Distance Run | Displacement | Average Velocity |
|-----------|--------------|--------------|------------------|
| 30.0 min | 7.7 km | 7.7 km | 0.26 km/min |

2. c
3. b.
4. d
5. c
6. a
7. Object B; the graph for Object B has a larger slope than that of Object A.
8. Object C has a negative slope and is, therefore, decelerating.
9. Object B started from rest with a velocity of zero. Object C slows to a stop ($v = 0$ m/s) and remains stopped.
10. Object D begins with negative velocity, crosses the axis and continues with positive velocity. This behavior indicates that it slows to a complete stop and then starts moving again.
11. Object A is moving forward (positive velocity) and Object E is moving backwards (negative velocity).

# Answer Key

## Section 3.2
## Motion with Constant Acceleration

**1.**

| Initial Conditions | | | Variables | | | Equation |
|---|---|---|---|---|---|---|
| $\Delta t$ | $d_f$ | $v_f$ | $\bar{a}$ | $d_i$ | $v_i$ | $v_f - v_i = at_i$ |
| 3.0 s | X | ? | 0.20 m/s$^2$ | X | 0.40 m/s | |

$$v_f - v_i = \bar{a}t_i$$
$$v_f = v_i + \bar{a}t_i$$
$$= 0.40 \text{ m/s} + (0.20 \text{ m/s}^2)(3.0 \text{ s})$$
$$= 1.0 \text{ m/s}$$

**2.**

| Initial Conditions | | | Variables | | | Equation |
|---|---|---|---|---|---|---|
| $t_f$ | $d_f$ | $v_f$ | $\bar{a}$ | $d_i$ | $v_i$ | $d_f = d_i + v_it_f + \frac{1}{2}at_f^2$ |
| ? | 45 m | X | 4.5 m/s2 | 0.0 m | 15 m/s | |

$$d_f = d_i + v_it_f + \frac{1}{2}\bar{a}t_f^2$$

$$45 \text{ m} = 0.0 \text{ m} + (15 \text{ m/s}) \, t_f + \frac{1}{2} \, (4.5 \text{ m/s}^2)t_f^2$$

$$(2.25 \text{ m/s}^2)t_f^2 + (15 \text{ m/s}) \, t_f - 45 \text{ m} = 0.0 \text{ m}$$

Using the quadratic equation,

$$t_f = \frac{-15 \text{ m/s} \pm \sqrt{(15 \text{ m/s})^2 - 4(225 \text{ m/s}^2)(-45 \text{ m})}}{2(225 \text{ m/s}^2)}$$

$$= 2.2 \text{ s}$$

**3.**

| Initial Conditions | | | Variables | | | Equation |
|---|---|---|---|---|---|---|
| $t_f$ | $d_f$ | $v_f$ | $\bar{a}$ | $d_i$ | $v_i$ | $d_f = d_i + v_it_f + \frac{1}{2}at_f^2$ |
| 3.0 s | ? | 15.0 m/s | X | 0.0 m | 10.0 m/s | |

$$d_f = d_i + v_it_f + \frac{1}{2}\bar{a}t_f^2$$

$$= 0.0 \text{ m} + (10 \text{ m/s})(3.0 \text{ s}) +$$
$$\frac{1}{2} \left( \frac{15.0 \text{ m/s} - 10.0 \text{ m/s}}{3.0 \text{ s} - 0.0 \text{ s}} \right)(3.0 \text{ s})^2$$

$$= 37 \text{ m}$$

**4.**

| Initial Conditions | | Variables | | | | Equation |
|---|---|---|---|---|---|---|
| $\Delta t$ | $d_f$ | $v_f$ | $\bar{a}$ | $d_i$ | $v_i$ | $v_f^2 = v_i^2 + 2a(d_f - d_i)$ |
| X | 35.0 m | ? | 4.5 m/s$^2$ | 0.0 m | 0.0 m/s | |

$$v_f^2 = v_i^2 + 2\bar{a}(d_f - d_i)$$
$$v_f = \sqrt{(0.0 \text{ m/s})^2 + 2(4.5 \text{ m/s}^2)(35.0 \text{ m} - 0.0 \text{ m})}$$
$$= 18 \text{ m/s}$$

## Section 3.3
## Free Fall

1. air resistance
2. true
3. the same
4. true
5. true
6. 29.4 m/s
7. true
8. true
9. 9.80 m/s$^2$
10. true

**11.**

| Variable | Time | | | | |
|---|---|---|---|---|---|
| | $t_1$ | $t_2$ | $t_3$ | $t_4$ | $t_5$ |
| $v$ | − | − | 0 | + | + |
| $a$ | + | + | + | + | + |

**12.** $v_1, v_5, v_2, v_4, v_3$

**13.**

| Variable | Time | | | | |
|---|---|---|---|---|---|
| | $t_1$ | $t_2$ | $t_3$ | $t_4$ | $t_5$ |
| $v$ | + | + | 0 | − | − |
| $a$ | − | − | − | − | − |

**14.** $v_1, v_5, v_2, v_4, v_3$

## Section 3-1 Quiz

1. Average acceleration is determined by a measurable time interval. Instantaneous acceleration is the change in velocity at an instant of time.

2. If the acceleration and velocity vectors are pointing in the same direction, the object is speeding up. If they are pointing in opposite directions, it is slowing down.

3. The slope of the line is the acceleration.

4.
$$\bar{a} = \frac{v_f - v_i}{\Delta t} = \frac{16 \text{ m/s} - 25 \text{ m/s}}{2.0 \text{ s}} = -4.5 \text{ m/s}^2$$

5. $m = \dfrac{\text{rise}}{\text{run}} = \dfrac{19 \text{ m/s}}{4.0 \text{ m/s}} = 4.8 \text{ m/s}^2$

   It is instantaneous acceleration.

## Section 3-2 Quiz

1. No, a position-time graph cannot be created from a velocity-time graph because a velocity-time graph does not contain information about position.

2. You can determine displacement by measuring the area under the curve. You can determine instantaneous acceleration by measuring the slope of a tangent.

3. $v_f = v_i + \bar{a}\Delta t = 5.0 \text{ m/s} + (1.5 \text{ m/s}^2)(5.2 \text{ s})$
$$= 13 \text{ m/s}$$

4. $d_f = d_i + v_i t_f + \dfrac{1}{2}\bar{a}t_f^2 = 15 \times 10^3 \text{ m} +$

$$(11 \text{ m/s})(1.0 \text{ min})\left(\frac{60 \text{ s}}{1 \text{ min}}\right) +$$

$$\frac{1}{2}(0.10 \text{ m/s}^2)\left(1.0 \text{ min}\left(\frac{60 \text{ s}}{1 \text{ min}}\right)\right)^2$$

$$\approx 15.8 \text{ km}$$

   The car is almost at the 16 km marker.

5. $v_f^2 = v_i^2 + 2\bar{a}(d_f - d_i) = (6.4 \text{ m/s})^2 +$
$$2(0.1 \text{ m/s}^2)(100 \text{ m})$$
$$v_f = \sqrt{(6.4 \text{ m/s})^2 + 2(0.1 \text{ m/s}^2)(100 \text{ m})} = 8 \text{ m/s}$$

## Section 3-3 Quiz

1. The value of $g$ depends on the force of gravity. It is not affected by an object's weight, what it is made of, the height it is dropped from, or whether it is thrown or dropped.

2. The sign depends on the coordinate system you choose. If you define upward as positive, $g$ is negative. If you define downward as positive, $g$ is positive.

3. Neither object is in free fall because both experience at least some air resistance. Free fall is the motion of a body when air resistance is negligible and the action can be accounted for by gravity alone. Due to its shape, the feather encounters greater air resistance than the ball.

4. The ball reaches its highest point when its velocity as seen from the ground is zero and it is about to fall back down. Defining the upward direction as positive,
$$v_f = v_i + \bar{a}t_f$$
$$t_f = \frac{v_f - v_i}{\bar{a}} = \frac{0.0 \text{ m/s} - 49 \text{ m/s}}{-9.80 \text{ m/s}^2} = 5.0 \text{ s}$$

5. $d_f = d_i + v_i t_f + \dfrac{1}{2}\bar{a}t_f^2 = 0.0 \text{ m} +$

$$(49 \text{ m/s})(5.0 \text{ s}) + \frac{1}{2}(-9.80 \text{ m/s}^2)(5.0 \text{ s})^2 = 120 \text{ m}$$

## Reinforcement

### Motion Diagrams

1.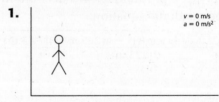

2.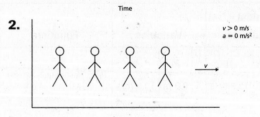

3.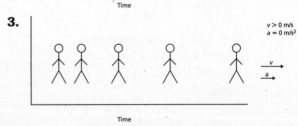

# Answer Key

**4.**

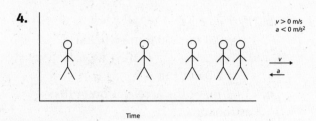

Time

## Enrichment

### Measuring Acceleration

1. Accelerometer 2. Elevator A is moving upward; its velocity is increasing between the 3rd and 4th floors.
2. Accelerometer 3. Elevator C is moving downward; its velocity is increasing between the 5th and 4th floors.
3. Accelerometer 1. Although it is in motion, Elevator B is not changing velocity between the 4th and 5th floors.
4. An elevator that is not moving or an elevator that is moving at a constant velocity would both have accelerometer readings of zero.
5. Accelerometer 3. The elevator would be in free fall and accelerating downward.
6. Accelerometer 3. The sudden stop would result from acceleration downward.
7. You could be moving upward at constant velocity, moving downward at constant velocity, or not moving.
8. No, because it would show zero acceleration in all three scenarios.
9. Accelerometer 1. The elevator would be stopped and the accelerometer would show no acceleration.
10. Yes, at the instant an elevator starts moving, it has a positive acceleration, but zero velocity.

## Transparency 3-1 Worksheet

### Velocity v. Time

1. The object is moving at constant velocity in Graph A. The velocity is 150.0 m/s.
2. The slope of the line in Graph B is 20.0 m/s$^2$ [velocity (m/s)/time (s)]. The slope represents the acceleration.

3. $v = 150.0$ m/s
4. $v = (20.0$ m/s$^2)t$
5. $\Delta d = \bar{v} t = (150.0$ m/s$)(4.5$ s$) = 680.0$ m
6. $\Delta d = \dfrac{1}{2}(v_f + v_i)(t)$

   $= \dfrac{1}{2}(1.00 \times 10^2$ m/s $+ 0.4 \times 10^2$ m/s$)(3.0$ s$)$

   $= 2.1 \times 10^2$ m
7. The object is moving with a velocity of 150.0 m/s in Graph A and with a velocity of 60.0 m/s in Graph B.
8. $v_f = v_i + at_f$
   $t_f = (v_f - v_i)/a$
   $= (150$ m/s $- 100$ m/s$)/(20$ m/s$)$
   $= 2.5$ s

   The object in Graph B will take 2.5 s more than the time at vi to reach 150 m/s.
   $5$ s $+ 2.5$ s $= 7.5$ s
9. $150$ m/s $- 40$ m/s $= 110$ m/s

## Transparency 3-2 Worksheet

## Positive and Negative Acceleration

1. 97 km/h = 97,000 m/h
   97,000 m/h/(60 min/h $\times$ 60 s/min) = 27 m/s
2. Car A: $\dfrac{27 \text{ m/s}}{6.0 \text{ s}} = 4.5$ m/s$^2$

   Car B: $\dfrac{27 \text{ m/s}}{10.0 \text{ s}} = 2.7$ m/s$^2$

   Car C: $\dfrac{27 \text{ m/s}}{8.0 \text{ s}} = 3.4$ m/s$^2$
3. Car A; highest acceleration
4. It is pointing in the same direction as the velocity. This shows an increased speed.
5. Any change in velocity is a form of acceleration. It is negative acceleration because the acceleration vector is pointing in the opposite direction as the velocity vector.
6. Car A, because it takes the shortest time to decelerate from 97 km/h to 0 km/h.

## Transparency 3-3 Worksheet

## Position, Velocity, and Acceleration Graphs

1. The slope of the line at a given point is the velocity at that point.

2. The time versus position graph shows an increasing slope, which indicates that the velocity is increasing. The time versus velocity graph also shows that the velocity is increasing.

3. $\Delta d = \Delta d_{rectangle} + \Delta d_{triangle}$

$$d_f = v_i(\Delta t) + \frac{1}{2}\bar{a}(\Delta t)^2$$

$$= (40.0 \text{ m/s})(2 \text{ s}) + \frac{1}{2}(20.0 \text{ m/s})(2 \text{ s})^2$$

$$= 120 \text{ m}$$

or 100 m to one significant digit

4. 120.0 m

5. They are the same because the area under a time versus velocity graph is the same as the displacement on the time versus position graph.

6. Acceleration is the change in velocity divided by the change in time, $\Delta v/\Delta t$. You can determine acceleration by solving the equation, $(v_{final} - v_{initial})/(t_{final} - t_{iniital})$.

7. The time versus velocity graph has a constant slope, which indicates that the acceleration is constant. Thus the time versus acceleration graph shows a constant acceleration.

8. The time versus position graph would be a straight line sloping upward. The time versus acceleration graph would be a straight, horizontal line at 0.

## Transparency 3-4 Worksheet

### Free Fall on the Moon

1. **a.** $v_f = v_i + \bar{a}t_f$
   $0 = (4.9 \text{ m/s}) + (-9.80 \text{ m/s}^2)t_f$
   $t_f = (-4.9 \text{ m/s})/(-9.80 \text{ m/s}^2)$
   $= 0.50 \text{ s}$

   **b.** 0 m/s

   **c.** 9.80 m/s² Even though the boy is not moving at that instant, he is still accelerating. He is accelerating downward.

2. **a.** $v_f = v_i + \bar{a}t_f$
   $0 = (16 \text{ m/s}) + (-1.62 \text{ m/s}^2)t_f$
   $t_f = (-16 \text{ m/s})/(-1.62 \text{ m/s}^2)$
   $= 9.9 \text{ s}$

**b.** $d_f = d_i + v_i t_f + 1/2\bar{a}t_f^2$
   $= 0.0 \text{ m} + (0.0 \text{ m/s})(9.9 \text{ s}) +$
   $\qquad 1/2(-1.62 \text{ m/s}^2)(9.9 \text{ s})^2$
   $= 8.0 \times 10^1 \text{ m}$

**c.** 1.62 m/s², the acceleration of the astronaut

**d.** They are different. Acceleration is downward; initial velocity is upward.

## Chapter 3 Chapter Assessment

### Accelerated Motion

### Understanding Physics Concepts

1. e
2. b
3. d
4. a
5. f
6. c
7. acceleration
8. true
9. slowing down
10. true
11. 9.80 m/s²
12. zero
13. downward
14. true
15. c
16. b
17. a
18. b
19. a
20. d
21. d
22. a

### Thinking Critically

1. $d_f = d_i + v_i t + \frac{1}{2}\bar{a}t^2$

$$= 0.0 \text{ m} + (0.0 \text{ m/s})(8.4 \text{ s}) +$$

$$\frac{1}{2}(0.50 \text{ m/s}^2)(8.4 \text{ s})^2$$

$$= 18 \text{ m/s}$$

**2.** **a.** Starting from rest, $d_i = 0.0$ m, $v_i = 0.0$ m/s.

$$d_f = d_i + v_i t + \frac{1}{2}\bar{a}t^2 = \frac{1}{2}\bar{a}t^2$$

$$\bar{a} = \frac{2d_f}{t^2}$$

$$= \frac{2(100.0 \text{ m})}{(4.5 \text{ s})^2}$$

$$= 9.9 \text{ m/s}^2$$

**b.**

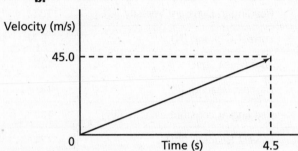

**3.** **a.** $v_f = v_i + \bar{a}t$
$$= 1.6 \text{ m/s} + (0.33 \text{ m/s}^2)(3.6 \text{ s})$$
$$= 2.8 \text{ m/s}$$

**b.** $d_f = d_i + v_i t + \frac{1}{2}\bar{a}t^2$

$$= 0.00 \text{ m} + (1.6 \text{ m/s})(3.6 \text{ s}) +$$
$$\frac{1}{2}(0.33 \text{ m/s}^2)(3.6 \text{ s})^2$$

$$= 7.9 \text{ m/s}$$

**5.** For the first 5.0 s, the velocity was constant. The object then increased velocity at a constant acceleration of 6.7 m/s$^2$ for 3.0 s. The object then decreased velocity at a constant acceleration of $-7.5$ m/s$^2$ for 4.0 s.

## Applying Physics Knowledge

**1.** The truck's speed increases as it backs down the ramp, so its velocity increases in the direction of motion. Therefore, its acceleration is positive and in the same direction as the velocity.

**2.** The instantaneous acceleration is the slope of the line.

**3.** The displacement is the area under a velocity-time graph. The graph in this case is a straight line, yielding a triangular area.

**4.** For an object in free fall, $a = g$.

**5.** **a.** $v_f = v_i + \bar{a}t_f$

$$t_f = \frac{v_f - v_i}{\bar{a}}$$

$$= \frac{0.0 \text{ m/s} - 45.0 \text{ m/s}}{-980 \text{ m/s}^2}$$

$$= 4.6 \text{ s}$$

**4.**

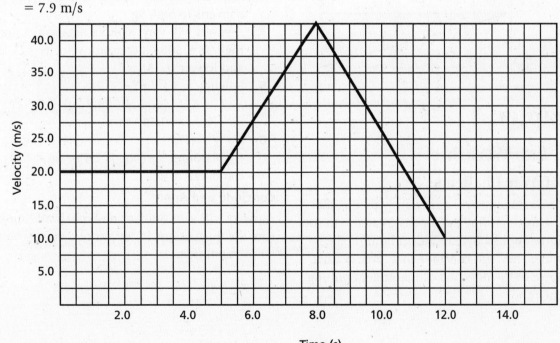

**b.** Since the rocket takes off from the ground, $d_i = 0.0$ m, and at its highest point, $v_f = 0.0$ m/s.

$$v_f^2 = v_i^2 + 2\bar{a}t_f(d_f - d_i)$$
$$0 = v_i^2 + 2\bar{a}t_f d_f$$
$$d_f = \frac{-v_i^2}{2\bar{a}t_f}$$
$$= \frac{-(450 \text{ m/s})^2}{2(-9.80 \text{ m/s}^2)(4.6 \text{ s})}$$
$$= 22 \text{ m}$$

**6. a.** Dropping the acorn from rest, $v_i = 0.0$ m/s, and as it ends up at rest on the ground, $d_f = 0.0$ m.

$$d_f = d_i + v_i t + \frac{1}{2}\bar{a}t^2 = d_i + \frac{1}{2}at^2$$
$$t = \sqrt{\frac{2(d_f - d_i)}{\bar{a}}}$$
$$= \sqrt{\frac{2(0.00 \text{ m} - 8.00 \text{ m})}{-9.80 \text{ m/s}^2}}$$
$$= 1.28 \text{ s}$$

**b.** $v_f = v_i + \bar{a}t_f$
$$= 0.0 \text{ m/s} + (-9.80 \text{ m/s}^2)(1.28 \text{ s})$$
$$= -12.5 \text{ m/s}$$

**c.**

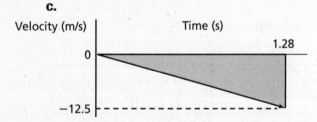

# Chapter 4

## Mini Lab Worksheet

### Tug-of-War Challenge

**1.** Most students will erroneously predict that the force pulling the rope is greater than the force applied by the student holding the rope. They will conclude that there is a net force in the direction of the student pulling the rope.

### Analyze and Conclude

**3.** Holding is the same as pulling. Even when your opponent starts moving, the forces in the rope are still at the same reading.

## Physics Lab
### Sample Data

| Force (N) | 10 N |
|---|---|
| Highest Reading (N) | 15 N |
| Reading at Constant Velocity (N) | 10 N |
| Lowest Reading (N) | 5 N |
| Your Mass (lbm) | 130 |
| Highest Reading (lbf) | 137 |
| Reading at constant velocity (lbf) | 130 |
| Lowest Reading (lbf) | 124 |

### Analyze

**1.** You need a net force to accelerate the mass upward. This causes the apparent weight to be greater than $mg$. The equation is $F_{scale} = mg + ma$.

**2.** The force must be less than $mg$, so $F_{scale} = mg - ma$.

**3.** Answers will vary. For sample data, 130 lbm converts to 58.8 kg

**4.** Answers will vary. Sample data values are highest $= 608$ N, constant velocity $= 578$ N, and lowest $= 551$ N.

**5.** Solving: $a = (F/m) - g$
$$= (608 \text{ N} / 58.8 \text{ kg}) - 9.80 \text{ m/s}^2$$
$$= 0.540 \text{ m/s}^2$$

**6.** $a = g - (F/m)$
$$= 9.80 \text{ m/s}^2 - (551 \text{ N} / 58.8 \text{ kg})$$
$$= 0.429 \text{ m/s}^2$$

### Conclude and Apply

Answers will vary. Student designs should measure the fluctuations in weight of a person on the amusement ride.

### Going Further

A bathroom scale actually measures the force it exerts upward on the person. It is confusing because the English system uses pounds for both mass and weight, and the metric system uses kilograms for both mass and weight. Though a scale can only measure force, it can also be used to measure mass by calibrating it based on the acceleration due to gravity.

### Real-World Physics

One *g*-force is the amount of force exerted by gravity on a mass at rest. A pilot pulling 6 *g*'s will undergo a force 6 times as great as force exerted by gravity when the pilot is at rest on the ground.

## Chapter 4 Study Guide

### Forces in One Dimension

### Vocabulary Review

1. external world
2. gravitational force
3. Newton's first law
4. force
5. field force
6. interaction pair
7. tension
8. net force
9. equilibrium
10. drag force
11. Newton's second law
12. apparent weight
13. contact force
14. Newton's third law
15. normal force
16. system
17. inertia
18. agent
19. free-body diagram
20. terminal velocity
21. weightlessness

## Section 4-1
## Force and Motion

1. true
2. false

3. true
4. false
5. true
6. false
7. false
8. true
9. d
10. b
11. c
12. d
13. c
14. c
15. a
16. d
17.

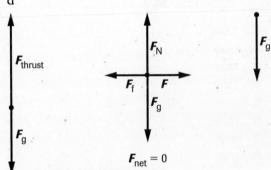

18. See answer art, above
19. See answer art, above

## Section 4-2
## Using Newton's Laws

1. c
2. d
3. a
4. g
5. f
6. b
7. h
8. e
9. a
10. b
11. b
12. c
13. c
14. a
15. direction opposite to
16. true
17. more
18. the drag force equals the force of gravity

## Section 4-3
## Interaction Forces

| Table 1 | | |
|---|---|---|
| **Force** | **Magnitude** | **Direction** |
| $F_{\text{book 1 on book 2}}$ | 40 N | down |
| $F_{\text{book 2 on book 1}}$ | 40 N | up |
| $F_{\text{book 2 on desktop}}$ | 50 N | down |
| $F_{\text{desktop on book 2}}$ | 50 N | up |
| $F_{\text{books 1 and 2 on desktop}}$ | 90 N | down |
| $F_{\text{desktop on books 1 and 2}}$ | 90 N | up |

1. false
2. true
3. true
4. false
5. true
6. false
7. true
8. true
9. true
10. true
11. false
12. true

## Section 4-1 Quiz

1. Force is a vector quantity, made up of both magnitude and direction.
2. The forces acting on an object must be combined using vector addition to find the net force on the object.
3. Equilibrium is when an object has no net forces acting upon it.
4. $a = \dfrac{F}{m} = \dfrac{270 \text{ N}}{35 \text{ kg}} = 7.7 \text{ m/s}^2$
5. $F_{\text{net}} = 240 \text{ N} + 120 \text{ N} = 360 \text{ N East}$
6. $m = \dfrac{F}{a} = \dfrac{970 \text{ N}}{4.4 \text{ m/s}^2} = 220 \text{ kg}$

## Section 4-2 Quiz

1. The weight of an object depends on the mass of the object and the acceleration due to gravity.

2. Terminal velocity is when the drag force on a falling object is equal to the gravitational force on that object.
3. Objects that are in free fall are considered weightless.
4. $F_{\text{net}} = 12,000.0 \text{ N} - 12,010.0 \text{ N} = -10.0 \text{ N}$, or 10.0 N acting to the South
5. **a.** $m = \dfrac{F}{g} = \dfrac{550 \text{ N}}{9.80 \text{ m/s}^2} = 56 \text{ kg}$

   $a = \dfrac{F}{m} = \dfrac{590 \text{ N}}{56 \text{ kg}} = 1.0 \times 10^1 \text{ m/s}^2$

   **b.** $a = \dfrac{F}{m} = \dfrac{510 \text{ N}}{56 \text{ kg}} = 9.1 \text{ m/s}^2$

## Section 4-3 Quiz

1. All forces are the result of the interaction between objects, specifically an agent and a system.
2. Tension is the specific name for the force exerted by a string or a rope.
3. Normal force is the support force resulting from the contact of two objects. It is perpendicular to the plane of contact between two objects.
4. From the interaction pair, the force the safe exerts on Earth is the same as what Earth exerts on the safe, namely its weight.
   $F = mg = (15,000 \text{ kg})(9.80 \text{ m/s}^2) =$

   $150,000 \text{ N}$

   $a = \dfrac{F}{m} = \dfrac{150,000 \text{ N}}{5.98 \times 10^{24} \text{ kg}} =$

   $2.5 \times 10^{-20} \text{ m/s}^2$
5. $T = mg + ma = (200.0 \text{ kg})(9.80 \text{ m/s}^2) +$
   $(200.0 \text{ kg})(1.2 \text{ m/s}^2) = 2200 \text{ N}$

## Chapter 4 Reinforcement

1. The fruit moved down to the base of the tines on the fork.
2. The fruit and the fork moved together because of a downward force exerted by the right arm. The left fist then exerted an upward force that stopped the motion of the hand and the fork. However, no such force was stopping the motion of the fruit, so the fruit continued moving down the tines. This situation is an example of Newton's first law.

The motion of the fruit was stopped when the fork exerted a force that stopped the fruit. The fruit was moving downward, and the force of the fork was in an upward direction. This upward unbalanced force caused an upward acceleration of the fruit, stopping its downward motion. This situation is an example of Newton's second law.

3. The fruit flew off the fork into the sink.

4. The explanation is the same as before, with one exception. In the first exercise, the fork exerted a force on the fruit, stopping its motion. In the second exercise, the fork did not exert a force on the fruit, so the fruit kept moving until it struck the sink.

## Chapter 4 Enrichment

### Procedure

1. The faster an object moves through the water, the higher the drag force will be.

2. Attach a length of string to a small object and attach the other end to a small spring scale. Fill the basin with water. Submerge the object at one end of the basin. Hold the other end of the scale at the far end of the basin. Pull the scale steadily away from the basin a distance of 30 cm in 4 s. Observe the spring scale as you do this and record the force. Repeat several times. Then repeat several times using a time of 2 s.

3. An irregularly shaped object will create a higher drag force than a streamlined one.

4. Attach a length of string to a small irregular object. Attach the other end to a small spring scale. Fill the basin with water. Submerge the object at one end of the basin. Hold the other end of the scale at the far end of the basin. Pull the scale steadily away from the basin a distance of 30 cm in 4 s. Observe the spring scale as you do this and record the force. Repeat several times. Then repeat several times with a streamlined object using the same distance and time.

### Results

1. The drag force (reading on the spring scale) was higher at higher speeds. The hypothesis was supported.

2. The drag force (reading on the spring scale) was higher for the irregularly shaped object. The hypothesis was supported.

3. The object may hit the bottom of the basin, adding drag. It is difficult to pull the scale at a constant speed and to read the scale while it is moving. Attaching the string at different points on the object may result in different data.

4. Measure the drag force using very cold water. Then do the same experiment except with very hot water. (If students do this experiment they will probably not see significant differences. They should not use excessively hot water because of the danger of burns.)

5. Hot water is less dense than cold water, so there should be less resistance. The difference in density is very small, so any differences in the drag force may not be measurable with this experiment.

## Transparency Worksheet 4-1

### Combining Forces on an Object

1.  a. $F_A$ represents the friction between the ground and the sled.
    b. $F_B$ represents the pull of the person on the sled.
    c. $F_C$ represents the pull of the rope on the sled.
    d. $F_D$ represents the pull of the rope on the person.
    e. $F_E$ represents the pull of the sled on the person.
    f. $F_F$ represents the friction between the person and the ground.

2. sled on ground, ground on sled; rope on sled, sled on rope; rope on person, person on rope; person on ground, ground on person

3. The net force that moves the sled is the force the person exerts on the ground minus the friction between the sled and the ground.

## Transparency Worksheet 4-2

### Motion and Newton's Second Law

1. $a = \Delta v/\Delta t$
   $= (3.0 \text{ km/h} - 0.0 \text{ km/h})/(0.75 \text{ h} - 0.0 \text{ h})$
   $= (3.0 \text{ km/h})/(0.75 \text{ km/h})$
   $= (3000 \text{ m})/((3600 \text{ s})(2700 \text{ s}))$
   $= 3.09 \times 10^{-4} \text{ m/s}^2$

2. $0 \text{ m/s}^2$

3. $a = \Delta v/\Delta t$
   $= (4.0 \text{ km/h} - 3.0 \text{ km/h})/(2.5 \text{ h} - 1.75 \text{ h})$
   $= (1 \text{ km/h})/(0.75 \text{ h})$
   $= (1000 \text{ m})/((3600 \text{ s})(2700 \text{ s}))$
   $= 1.0 \times 10^{-4} \text{ m/s}$

4. $1.1 \text{ m/s}$

5. $a = F/m$
   $F = ma$
   $= (3.1 \times 10^{-4} \text{ m/s}^2)(120,000 \text{ kg})$
   $= 37 \text{ N}$

6. $F = ma$
   $= (0 \text{ m/s}^2)(120,000 \text{ kg})$
   $= 0 \text{ N}$

7. $F = ma$
   $= (1.0 \times 10^{-4} \text{ m/s}^2)(120,000 \text{ kg})$
   $= 12 \text{ N}$

8. $1.2 \times 10^{-4} \text{ m/s}^2$

## Transparency Worksheet 4-3

### Newton's Third Law: Interaction Pairs

1. the hand, the bowling ball, and Earth

2. $F_{\text{hand on bowling ball}}$ is the force that the hand exerts upward on the bowling ball.

   $F_{\text{bowling ball on hand}}$ is the force that Earth exerts downward on the bowling ball.

   $F_{\text{bowling ball on Earth}}$ is the force that the bowling ball exerts upward on Earth.

3. $F_{\text{hand on bowling ball}}$ and $F_{\text{bowling ball on hand}}$; $F_{\text{Earth on bowling ball}}$ and $F_{\text{bowling ball on Earth}}$. They are interaction pairs because they are of equal magnitude and opposite direction and act on different objects.

4. $F_{\text{bowling ball on hand}}$ acts only on the hand, $F_{\text{bowling ball on Earth}}$ acts only on Earth, and $F_{\text{hand on bowling ball}}$ and $F_{\text{Earth on bowling ball}}$ act only on the bowling ball.

5. The movement of the ball is due to unbalanced forces on it, not the balanced force of interaction pairs that act on each object.

## Transparency Worksheet 4-4

### Weight and Normal Force

1. Weight is the force defined by the formula $F_g = mg$, where weight is a force caused by the acceleration due to gravity on a mass.

2. The normal force is a support force resulting from the contact of two objects. It is always perpendicular to the plane of contact between the two objects.

3. The weight of the box and the magnitude of the normal force are equal in Figure a.

4. The magnitude of the normal force is greater than the weight of the box in Figure b.

5. External forces other than gravity and the mass of the object may change the normal force that an object exerts.

6. The box's apparent weight is different from the weight caused by its mass and gravity in Figures b and c.

## Chapter 4 Assessment

### Forces

#### Understanding Physics Concepts

1. b
2. a
3. c
4. b
5. a
6. a
7. b
8. c
9. c
10. c
11. force
12. magnitude
13. away from

14. vector
15. equilibrium
16. gravity
17. weightlessness
18. velocity (or motion), surface area (or shape)
19. interactions
20. magnitude, opposite
21. rope (or string, cable, wire, etc.)
22. normal

**Thinking Critically**

1. The weight of any object is equal to the product of the mass of the object and the acceleration due to gravity. Mass does not change, but weight is dependent upon the gravitational force. The force of gravity on Mars is different from the force of gravity on Earth, so objects would have the same mass on Mars but a different weight.

2. As the elevator slows, your acceleration is in the direction opposite to your velocity. The direction of the acceleration of the elevator is down. Thus the net force on you is downward. Your apparent weight is equal to an upward force equal to your weight plus the net force acting on you. In this case, the net force is downward, so your apparent weight would be $F_g - F_{net}$. Your apparent weight would decrease.

3. No, there is no net force on the boat because it has neither vertical nor horizontal acceleration. There is, however, constant forward motion because the force of tension is greater than the force of friction.

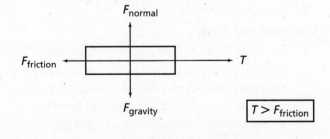

$$T > F_{friction}$$

4. Interaction pairs are forces that act on different objects; they are equal in magnitude but opposite in direction. The drawing shows an interaction pair in the force of gravity from the weight of the boat balanced by the normal force of the boat on the ground.

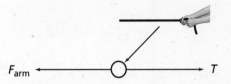

$$T = F_{arm}$$

5. The forces exerted by your arm muscles and the force exerted by the rope are acting on your hand.

6. Have the pilot take the jump plane to a higher altitude.

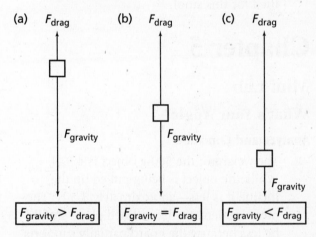

**Applying Physics Knowledge**

1. $F = ma = (6.0 \text{ kg})(2.0 \text{ m/s}^2) = 12 \text{ N}$

2. $m = \dfrac{F_g}{g} = \dfrac{30.0 \text{ N}}{9.80 \text{ m/s}^2} = 3.06 \text{ kg}$

3. $F_T = F_g$ and $F_g = mg$
   Therefore,
   $F_T = mg = (4.2 \text{ kg})(9.80 \text{ m/s}^2) = 41 \text{ N}$

4. A force of $-125$ N acting in the opposite direction will produce equilibrium.

5. $F_T = F_{net} + F_g$
   $= ma + mg = m(a + g)$
   $= (1.10 \times 10^3 \text{ kg})(0.45 \text{ m/s}^2 + 9.80 \text{ m/s}^2)$
   $= 1.1 \times 10^4 \text{ N}$

**6. a.** $m = \dfrac{F_g}{g} = \dfrac{2.0 \times 10^7 \text{ N}}{9.80 \text{ m/s}^2} = 2.0 \times 10^6 \text{ kg}$

**b.** $a = \dfrac{F_{thrust}}{m} = \dfrac{25 \times 10^6 \text{ N}}{2.0 \times 10^6 \text{ kg}} = 13 \text{ m/s}^2$

**7. a.** $m_1 = \dfrac{F_{1g}}{g} = \dfrac{25 \text{ N}}{9.80 \text{ m/s}^2} = 2.6 \text{ kg}$

$m_2 = \dfrac{F_{2g}}{g} = \dfrac{47 \text{ N}}{9.80 \text{ m/s}^2} = 4.8 \text{ kg}$

$a = \dfrac{F}{m_1 + m_2} = \dfrac{25 \text{ N}}{2.6 \text{ kg} + 4.8 \text{ kg}} = 3.4 \text{ m/s}^2$

**b.** $F_{cord} = m_2 a = (2.6 \text{ kg})(3.4 \text{ m/s}^2) = 8.8 \text{ N}$

**8.** $F_{welder} = mg = (102 \text{ kg})(9.80 \text{ m/s}^2)$
$= 1.00 \times 10^3 \text{ N}$

$F_{total} = (m_{welder} + m_{equipment})g$
$= (102 \text{ kg} + 14 \text{ kg})(9.80 \text{ m/s}^2) = 1100 \text{ N}$

Adding the torch and fuel tank to the weight of the welder would exceed the 1100 N specified for this stool.

# Chapter 5

## Mini Lab

### What's Your Angle?

#### Analyze and Conclude

**2.** The weight of the 500-g object is 4.9 N. While the object is being pulled up the incline it is less—approximately 3.5 N. The measurement on the inclined plane should be less because the board partially supports the object's weight.

**3.** $F_x = mg \sin \theta = (0.5 \text{ kg})(9.80 \text{ m/s}^2)(\sin 45°)$
$= 3.5 \text{ N}$

**4.** Answers may vary, although the inclined plane reading should be nearly the same as the component from question 3.

## Physics Lab

### The Coefficient of Friction

**Sample Data**

Object material = wood

Surface material = wood

**Data Table 1**

| $F_N$ (N) | Static Friction Force, $F_s$ (N) | | | |
|---|---|---|---|---|
| | Trial 1 | Trial 2 | Trial 3 | Average |
| 2.1 | 1.5 | 1.7 | 1.4 | 1.5 |

**Data Table 2**

| $F_N$ (N) | Kinetic Friction Force, $F_f$ (N) | | | |
|---|---|---|---|---|
| | Trial 1 | Trial 2 | Trial 3 | Average |
| 2.10 | 0.85 | 0.65 | 0.75 | 0.75 |

**Data Table 3**

| $F_N$ (N) | $F_s$ (N) | $F_f$ (N) | $\mu_s$ | $\mu_k$ |
|---|---|---|---|---|
| 2.10 | 1.53 | 0.75 | 0.73 | 0.36 |

**Data Table 4, Angle, $\theta$, when sliding begins on an incline**

| $\theta$ | $\tan \theta$ |
|---|---|
| 21° | 0.38 |

### Analyze

**1.** Answers are in Tables 1 and 3.

**2.** Answers are in Tables 2 and 3.

**3.** Answer is in Table 3.

**4.** Answer is in Table 3.

**5.** Answer is in Table 4.

### Conclude and Apply

**1.** Students should draw on their experience moving objects and conclude that the force necessary to start an object moving usually is greater than the force needed to keep it moving, so the value for $\mu_s$ is larger than for $\mu_k$. It is reasonable that $\mu_s > \mu_k$.

**2.**

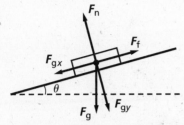

**3.** tan $\theta$ represents the coefficient of kinetic friction, because, tan $\theta = F_f/F_{gy} = F_f/F_N = \mu_k$

**4.** The value for tan $\theta$ and $\mu_k$ should be similar. The value for $\mu_s$ should be larger than tan $\theta$ and $\mu_k$.

## Going Further

Answers will vary depending on materials selected. Values for $\mu$ in the classroom, however, are most likely between 0 and 1.

## Real-World Physics

Because tan $\theta = \mu_k$, as long as the skier descends at a constant speed, only the angle of the hill needs to be observed.

# Study Guide

## Forces in Two Dimensions

### Vocabulary Review

1. component
2. static friction
3. equilibrant
4. kinetic friction
5. coefficient of kinetic friction
6. vector resolution
7. coefficient of static friction

## Section 5.1
## Vectors

1. true
2. velocity
3. true
4. true

**5.** may or may not be

**6.** true

**7.** tip

**8.**

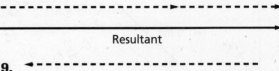

**9.**

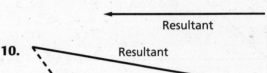

**10.**

**11.**

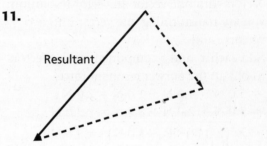

**12.** a

**13.** b

**14.** b

**15.** 11 m, 63° north of east

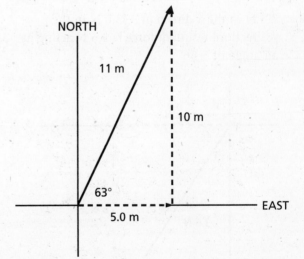

**16.** 43° north of east, 641 m/s

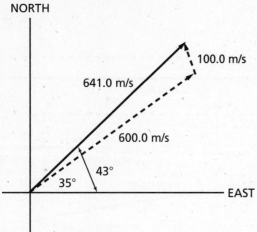

**17.** In vector addition you are transforming two vectors into one vector. In vector resolution you are transforming one vector into two vectors.

**18.** Add each $x$- and $y$-component of the vectors to obtain the answer resultant force,

$F_x = 5.0 \text{ N} - 4.0 \text{ N} + 1.0 \text{ N} = 2.0 \text{ N}$

$F_y = 3.0 \text{ N} + 2.0 \text{ N} - 8.0 \text{ N} = -3.0 \text{ N}$

$R = \sqrt{(2.0 \text{ N})^2 + (-3.0 \text{ N})^2} = 3.6 \text{ N}$

$\dfrac{R}{\sin\theta} = \dfrac{A}{\sin\alpha}$

$\sin\theta = \dfrac{A\sin\theta}{R} = \dfrac{(-3.0 \text{ N})\sin90°}{3.6 \text{ N}} = -0.83$

$\theta = -56°$

2.0 N in the $x$-direction, $-3.0$ N in the $y$-direction, resultant force is 3.6 N acting at an angle of $-56°$

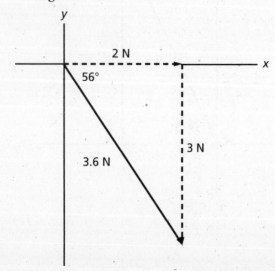

**19.** 2
**20.** 4
**21.** 1
**22.** 3

## Section 5.2
## Friction

**1.** c
**2.** b
**3.** c
**4.** c
**5.** b.
**6.**

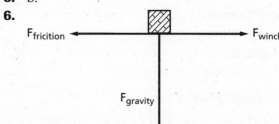

**7.** $F_{net} = F_{winch} - F_{friction}$
$= 2000 \text{ N} - (0.2)(9800 \text{ N}) = 40 \text{ N}$

**8.** $a = \dfrac{F}{m} = \dfrac{40 \text{ N}}{1000 \text{ kg}} = 0.04 \text{ m/s}^2$

## Section 5.3
## Force and Motion in Two Dimensions

**1.** c
**2.** c
**3.** b

**4.** $\dfrac{R}{\sin\theta} = \dfrac{A}{\sin\alpha}$

$A = \dfrac{(9.8 \text{ N})\sin25°}{\sin90°} = 4.1 \text{ N}$

$B = \sqrt{R^2 - A^2} = \sqrt{(9.8 \text{ N})^2 - (4.1 \text{ N})^2} = 8.8 \text{ N}$

The horizontal component is 4.1 N and the vertical component is 8.8 N

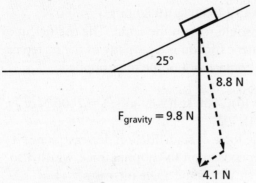

**5.** The *x*-component is 0 N and the *y*-component is 9.8 N

**6.** 8.8 N

**7.** $F_f = \mu_k F_N = (0.25)(8.8 \text{ N}) = 2.2 \text{ N}$

**8.** $F_{net} = F_{gravity} - F_{friction}$
$= 4.1 \text{ N} - (0.25)(8.8 \text{ N}) = 1.9 \text{ N}$

**9.** $a = \dfrac{F}{m} = \dfrac{1.9 \text{ N}}{1.0 \text{ kg}} = 1.9 \text{ m/s}^2$

**10.**

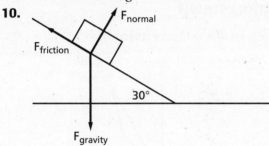

**11.**

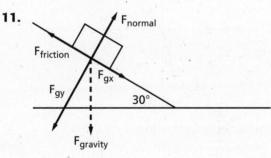

**12.** $\dfrac{R}{\sin \theta} = \dfrac{A}{\sin \alpha}$

$A = \dfrac{(200.0 \text{ kg})(9.80 \text{ m/s}^2)\sin 30°}{\sin 90°}$

$= 9.80 \times 10^2 \text{ N}$

$B = \sqrt{R^2 - A^2}$

$= \sqrt{(1960 \text{ N})^2 - (9.80 \times 10^2 \text{ N})^2}$

$= 1.70 \times 10^3 \text{ N}$

$F_{friction} = \mu_s F_{normal}$

$\mu_s = \dfrac{9.80 \times 10^2 \text{ N}}{1.70 \times 10^3 \text{ N}} = 0.6$

## Section 5-1 Quiz

**1.** Approximately 79 km, 43° east of north.

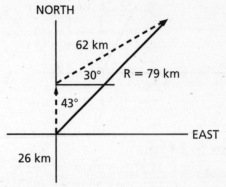

**2.** The teacher's question was ambiguous. Does "total" mean total distance or total displacement? The total distance traveled would simply be scalar (4 paces + 2 paces = 6 paces) but the total displacement would require vector addition (4 paces − 2 paces = 2 paces).

**3.** $F_y = R \sin \theta = (80 \text{ N}) \sin 60° = 70 \text{ N}$
$F_x = R \cos \theta = (80 \text{ N}) \cos 60° = 40 \text{ N}$

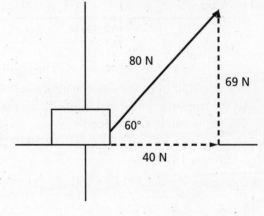

**4.** $R^2 = A^2 + B^2 - 2AB \cos \theta$

$R = \sqrt{(10 \text{ km})^2 + (20 \text{ km})^2 - 2(10 \text{ km})(20 \text{ km}) \cos (135°)} = 30 \text{ km}$

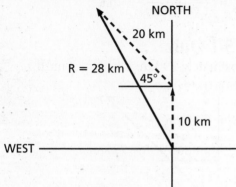

## Section 5-2 Quiz

**1.** $F_{parallel} = (525 \text{ N})(\sin 30.0°) = 262 \text{ N}$;
$F_{normal} = (525 \text{ N})(\cos 30.0°) = 455 \text{ N}$

**2.** increases

**3.**

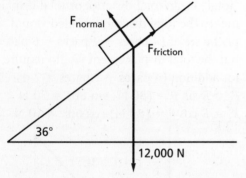

**4.** $F_{resultant} = 32 \text{ N} - 26 \text{ N} = 6 \text{ N}$; The equilibrant would have the same magnitude but in the opposite of the resultant, $F_{eq} = -6 \text{ N}$ (in the negative x-direction)

**5.** $F_{normal} = (30.0 \text{ kg})(9.80 \text{ m/s}^2)\cos 60.0°$
$= 147 \text{ N}$

$F_{friction} = \mu F_{normal} = (0.250)(147 \text{ N})$
$= 36.8 \text{ N}$

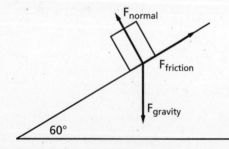

## Section 5-3 Quiz

**1.** $F_{friction} = \mu F_{normal} =$
$(0.45)(200.0 \text{ kg})(9.80 \text{ m/s}^2) = 880 \text{ N}$

**2.** It would remain the same. The coefficient of kinetic friction is a property of the materials in contact, not of the force applied.

**3.** $F_{friction} = \mu F_{normal} =$
$(0.10)(2500 \text{ kg})(9.80 \text{ m/s}^2) = 2400 \text{ N}$ or
$2.4 \times 10^3$

**4.** The force of static friction decreases since it depends upon the normal force, which also decreases as the angle increases.

**5.** It decreases, since the coefficient of kinetic friction is generally smaller than that of static friction.

**6.** Answers will vary. Letting out air will increase surface area of contact, but the force of friction does not depend upon area of contact.

## Reinforcement

### Forces in Two Dimensions

**1.** Measured, approximately 5.2 cm

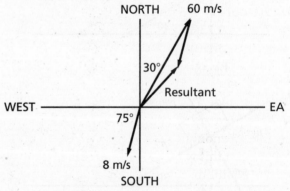

**2.** Measured, approximately 52 m/s

**3.** Measured, approximately 32°

**4.** 32° north of east; or, 58° east of north

## Enrichment

### Forces in Two Dimensions

1. Measured, approximately 97°, 41°, and 41°

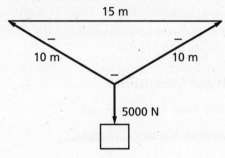

15 m

10 m        10 m

5000 N

2. $\theta = \cos^{-1}\dfrac{A^2 + B^2 - R^2}{2AB}$

$= \cos^{-1}\left(\dfrac{(10.0 \text{ m})^2 + (10.0 \text{ m})^2 - (15.0 \text{ m})^2}{2(10.0 \text{ m})(10.0 \text{ m})}\right)$

$= 97.2°$

$\theta =$

$= \cos^{-1}\left(\dfrac{(10.0 \text{ m})^2 + (15.0 \text{ m})^2 - (10.0 \text{ m})^2}{2(10.0 \text{ m})(15.0 \text{ m})}\right)$

$= 41.4°$

3. $T_x = T \sin 48.6° = 0.750T$
   $T_y = T \cos 48.6° = 0.661T$

4. $2(0.6614T) = 5.00 \times 10^3$ N

5. $T_{max} = 0.750T = (0.750)(5.00 \times 10^3 \text{ N})$
   $= 3750$ N

6. $\dfrac{5.00 \times 10^3 \text{ N}}{2 \text{ wires}} = 2500$ N

7. To provide a horizontal force component that prevents the sculpture from oscillating like a pendulum.

8. Yes, but this would require a recalculation of the equilibrium forces and the tension in each wire. As long as the wires could handle the maximum tension, a symmetrical suspension is not required.

9. No; the wire making the smaller angle with the perpendicular would have the greater tension.

10. Yes; the procedure is the same but with two different equilibrium conditions, one for each wire. The symmetrical suspension merely simplifies the calculations.

## Transparency Worksheet 5-1

### Vector Components

1. The vectors are not perpendicular. The angle between them is 110° (120.0° − 10.0°).

2. First, $a_1$ and $a_2$ are decomposed into components. Second, the vertical components of $a_1$ and $a_2$ are added. Then the horizontal components of $a_1$ and $a_2$ are added together. Third, the sum of the horizontal components and the sum of the vertical components are added to find the resultant vector.

3. $a_{2x}$ is negative because it points to the left.

4. $a_2$ has a larger vertical component.

5. $a_1$ has a larger horizontal component.

6. $a_{1x} = a_1 \cos 10°$     $a_{1y} = \sin 10°$

7. $a_{2x} = a_2 \cos 120°$     $a_{2y} = a_2 \sin 120°$

8. $a_{net} = \sqrt{(a_{net\,x}^2 + a_{net\,y}^2)}$, $\theta = \tan^{-1}\left(\dfrac{a_{net\,y}}{a_{net\,x}}\right)$

9. $a_{net} = (\sqrt{a_{net\,x}^2 + a_{net\,y}^2})$

   $= \sqrt{(7.8 \text{ km})^2 + (9.0 \text{ km})^2}$

   $= 12$ km

   $\theta = \tan^{-1}\left(\dfrac{9.0 \text{ km}}{7.8 \text{ km}}\right)$

   12 km at 49°

## Transparency Worksheet 5-2

### Surfaces and Friction

1. $(9.80 \text{ m/s}^2)(2 \text{ kg})(0.50) = 10$ N

2. $(9.80 \text{ m/s}^2)(2 \text{ kg})(0.20) = 4$ N

3. Yes, the force of static friction is 40 N × 0.90 = 36 N ≈ 40 N, less than the horizontal force.

4. The roughness of the surfaces makes than hard to slide past each other.

5. The surface of the paper is not perfectly smooth, but it also does not have sharp projections that would give it a high coefficient of friction.

6. The coefficients of static and kinetic friction would be relatively high because of the roughness of the surface of the sandpaper.

## Transparency Worksheet 5-3

### Static Friction

1. $F_N = F_g$
   $= mg$
   $= (20 \text{ kg})(9.80 \text{ m/s}^2)$
   $= 200 \text{ N}$

2. The static friction force gradually increases.

3. The forces are equal. If they were not equal, there would be a net force and the toboggan would move.

4. $F_{f, \text{static}} = \mu_s F_N$
   $= (0.20)(196 \text{ N})$
   $= 39 \text{ N}$

5. Yes, the pulling force is greater than the maximum static friction force.

6. $F_{f, \text{kinetic}} = \mu_k F_N$
   $= (0.15)(196 \text{ N})$
   $= 29 \text{ N}$

7. $a = (F_p - F_f)/m$
   $= (50 \text{ N} - 29.4 \text{ N})/20 \text{ kg}$
   $= 1 \text{ m/s}^2$

8. $F_N = (35 \text{ kg})(9.80 \text{ m/s}^2)$
   $= 343 \text{ N}$

   $F_{f, \text{kinetic}} = (0.20)(343 \text{ N})$
   $= 69 \text{ N}$

   No. The maximum static friction force would be 68.6 N, which is greater than the pulling force.

## Transparency Worksheet 5-4

### Forces on an Inclined Plane

1. The process is called vector decomposition.

2. F is a single force vector acting in a certain direction. $F_x$ is its horizontal component and $F_y$ is its vertical component.
   $F_x^2 + F_y^2 = F^2$

3. $F_x$ would point to the left, $F_y$ would be the same, and F would lie between $F_x$ and $F_y$.

4. $F_y = \sqrt{F^2 - F_x^2}$

5. If the angle is increased to 40°, $F_y$ would increase and $F_x$ would decrease.

6. Earth's gravity causes $F_g$, which is the weight of the trunk. The vector points downward because gravity acts towards Earth's center.

7. $F_{gx}$ would decrease and $F_{gy}$ would increase.

8. $F_{gy} = -F_g \cos \theta$

9. $F_{gx} = -F_g \sin \theta$

10. The inclined plane exerts an upward force, $F_N$, on the trunk that is equal in magnitude to $F_{gy}$ and acts perpendicular to the surface of the inclined plane.

## Chapter Assessment

### Forces in Two Dimensions

### Understanding Physics Concepts

1. c
2. c
3. c
4. a
5. a
6. c
7. b
8. c
9. b
10. b

11.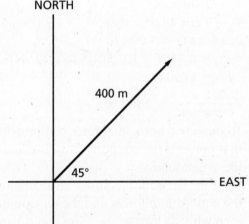

12. $A_x = A \cos \theta = (500.0 \text{ N})(\cos 30.0°)$
    $= 433 \text{ N}$

    $A_y = A \sin \theta = (500.0 \text{ N})(\sin 30.0°)$
    $= 2.50 \times 10^2 \text{ N}$

13. $A = \sqrt{R^2 - B^2} =$
    $\sqrt{(10.0 \text{ m/s})^2 - (2.00 \text{ m/s})^2} = 9.80 \text{ m/s}$

14. $R^2 = A^2 + B^2 - 2AB \cos \theta$
    $R = \sqrt{(4.0 \text{ m})^2 + (3.0 \text{ m})^2 - 2(4.0 \text{ m})(3.0 \text{ m}) \cos (142°)} = 6.6 \text{ m}$

15. $\theta = \sin^{-1} \left( \dfrac{(3.00 \text{ m})(\sin 27.0°)}{4.00 \text{ m}} \right) = 20.0°$

## Thinking Critically

1. Depending on the length and direction of the two vectors, the resultant could be in any quadrant. More information is required before an answer can be determined.

2. No; the force of friction does not depend on the surface area of contact. Only the coefficient of friction and the normal force determine the force of friction.

3. Subtracting a vector means adding the negative of the vector. The negative of a vector has the same length as the original vector, but points in the opposite direction. The order of the subtraction does matter, since the vector with the largest magnitude will determine the direction of the resultant.

4. Measured, Resultant = 101 N, 14° south of west
   Equilibrant = 101 N, 14° north of east

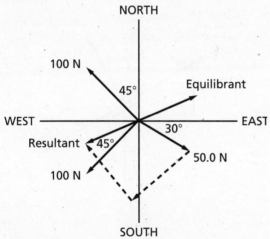

5. Yes; when two surfaces are in contact (static), their molecules have more of a chance to bond than they would if they were in motion (kinetic), resulting in a greater frictional force.

6. Yes; the time involved in molecular bonding is negligible when compared to the motion of the respective surfaces.

7. No; according to this theory, a greater surface area would result in a correspondingly greater frictional force as it would provide more points of bonding for the surface molecules.

## Applying Physics Knowledge

1. $\mu = \dfrac{F_{\text{friction}}}{F_{\text{norm}}} =$

   $$\dfrac{(5.00\times10^2 \text{ N})(\sin 25°)}{(5.00\times10^2 \text{ N})(\cos 25°)} = 0.47$$

2. Measured, approximately 264 m/s, 6° west of north

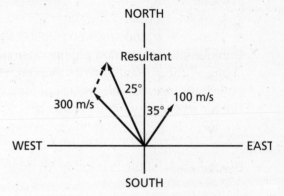

3. **a.** Because the frictional force is constant, the acceleration will be constant. Therefore, use the equations for constant acceleration: $a = \dfrac{v_f^2 - v_i^2}{2d}$

   Given:
   $v_i = 6.7$ m/s
   $v_f = 0$ m/s
   $d = 18$ m
   Therefore,
   $$a = \dfrac{v_f^2 - v_i^2}{2d}$$
   $$= \dfrac{0 \text{ m/s}^2 - 6.7\text{m/s}^2}{2(18 \text{ m})}$$
   $$= -1.2 \text{ m/s}^2$$
   The magnitude of frictional force is:
   $F_k = ma = (0.114 \text{ kg})(1.2 \text{ m/s}^2)$
   $= 0.14$ N

3. **b.** To find the frictional force, use
   $F = \mu_k N$
   Considering the vertical direction, there are two forces acting on the puck, the force of gravity (or the puck's weight) and the normal force. These two forces must add to zero.
   $N - mg = 0 \rightarrow N = mg$

Therefore,

$$F = \mu_k N = \mu_k mg$$

$$\mu_k = \frac{F}{mg} = \frac{ma}{mg} = \frac{a}{g}$$

$$= \frac{1.4}{9.80} = 0.14$$

**4.** First convert the mass of the sign to newtons:

$F_g = 1000.0$ kg (mass), weight =
$$1000.0 \times 9.80 = 9.80 \times 10^3 \text{ N}$$

There is only one upward pulling cable supplying all the upward force on the sign. This cable pulls upward with 9800 N of force. The force of tension on this cable is:

$$F_{tension} = \frac{F_{gravity}}{\sin \theta}$$

Use the Angle of the Resolution Vector to find $\theta$:

$$\theta = \tan^{-1}\left(\frac{\text{opposite side}}{\text{adjacent side}}\right) = \tan^{-1}\left(\frac{3}{4}\right)$$

$$\theta = 36.9°$$

Then solve for $F_{tension}$:

$$F_{tension} = \frac{F_{gravity}}{\sin \theta} = \frac{9.80 \times 10^3 \text{ N}}{\sin 36.9°}$$

$$= 16,300 \text{ N}$$

**5.** $9.5 \text{ N} = W \sin \theta + F_{friction}$

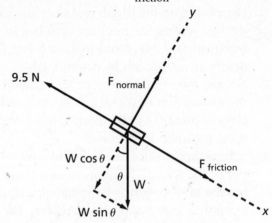

**6.**
$$7.0 \text{ N} = W \sin \theta - F_{friction}$$
$$9.5 \text{ N} - F_{friction} = 7.0 \text{ N} + F_{friction}$$
$$2F_{friction} = 2.5 \text{ N}$$
$$F_{friction} = 1.2 \text{ N}$$

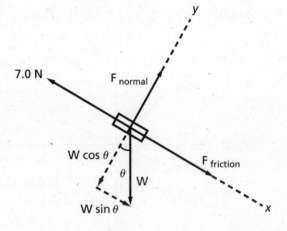

*Physics: Principles and Problems*